Auto radiograph at sub-cellular level shows *Tradescantia* labeled with tritiated thymidine. The uneven label indicates that DNA synthesis occurred at different times in different parts of the chromosomes.

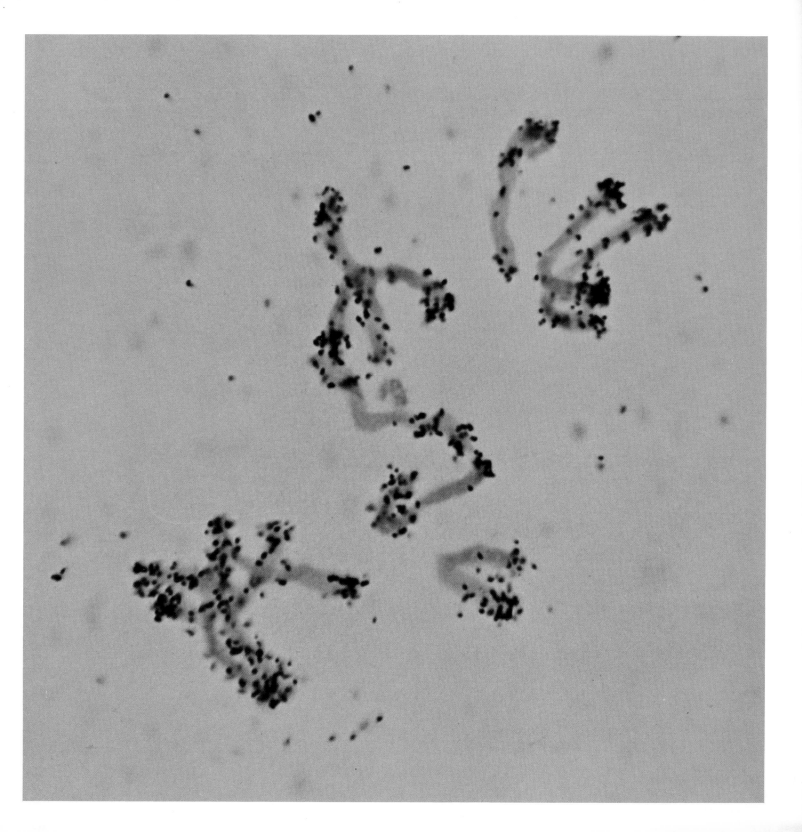

Radioisotopes and Radiation

Recent Advances in Medicine, Agriculture, and Industry

John H. Lawrence, M.D.

Director, Donner Laboratory
and Donner Pavilion
University of California (Berkeley)

Bernard Manowitz

Head, Radiation Division
Nuclear Engineering Department
Brookhaven National Laboratory

Benjamin S. Loeb

Assistant to the Director
Division of Technical Information
United States Atomic Energy Commission

32568

McGraw-Hill Book Company
New York San Francisco Toronto London

This volume is dedicated
to the memory of President John F. Kennedy
whose interest in science,
as in all the arts of living,
was deep, productive, and inspiring.

Foreword

The dedication of these volumes to John F. Kennedy is most appropriate to convey the continuing admiration of his still-sorrowing countrymen.

President Kennedy personified, both personally and as our President, the long devotion of the people of the United States to the conviction that human knowledge should be dedicated to the betterment of the human condition on this earth—for men of all nations. In his words and his works, the late President conveyed this spirit to the world eloquently and effectively.

The achievement of nuclear fission was the work of many scientists from many nations, brought to fruition through the achievement of the nuclear chain reaction in the United States. From the beginning of the era of atomic science, it has been the hope and the determined purpose of the American people that this great advance of human knowledge be directed to man's betterment in every land. Administrations have changed but our goals and resolution to attain those goals have remained unchanged. We continue steadfast in our commitments now, believing that in the further exploration of the atom lies the likelihood of discoveries to strengthen our hopes for peace.

After little more than two decades, the prospects and promises for tangible realization of our dreams for peaceful uses of the atom are brightening. Benefits are already being enjoyed by many citizens of many lands. Under a continuing climate of peace, we may hope and expect that those benefits will multiply and touch vastly greater numbers of lives throughout the world—through cheaper and more abundant electricity, through improvements in agriculture, through more efficient industry, and through life-saving advances in the understanding, prevention and treatment of disease. These achievements —and many more—will contribute to bringing humanity nearer the realization of a life of universal dignity and opportunity for all peoples in a world freed of poverty, hunger, illness and war.

We of the United States are proud of the contributions we have been able to make toward these thrilling advances in man's capacities. We take greater satisfaction, however, from the fact that the development of nuclear energy continues to afford the basis for both a new kind and a new spirit of international cooperation in the exchange of scientific knowledge and the evolving of more universal goals for peaceful applications of such knowledge. The Geneva Conferences in 1955, 1958, and now again in 1964, the excellent work of the International Atomic Energy Agency, and the many other exchanges and contacts of recent years represent a trend in relations between nations as full of portent as the advent of nuclear science itself.

We believe the continuing effort of the United States for peace in the world will be strengthened by our continuing effort to work with other nations to develop and apply peaceful uses for nuclear energy for the betterment of all men, wherever or however they live on this planet. The policies of the Government of the United States in this regard represent and reflect the purposes in the hearts of the American people.

Lyndon B. Johnson

The White House
May 1964

Table of Contents

Preface

The discovery of artificial radioactivity and of methods for the large-scale production of radioisotopes stimulated many people to use them, along with machine-produced electromagnetic and particulate radiations, in research in many fields. With these investigations came the promise of a large variety of advances in medicine, agriculture and industry. So many have in fact been found that to cover them adequately would require many volumes. Our task, to cover them in the brief compass of the present volume, has accordingly imposed on us the need to be highly selective in the choice of subject matter. We have attempted therefore to review and evaluate certain lines of work which seem to us to have advanced significantly since the last (1958) Geneva Conference on Peaceful Uses of Atomic Energy.

We have based our selections on many discussions with our colleagues. Nevertheless, the choice of subject matter in the last analysis reflects our particular spheres of interest. Inevitably, many important contributions have been left out. To those of our colleagues whose work may thus have been slighted we must apologize and plead exigencies of time and space.

Limitations in space have required arbitrariness not only in content but also in treatment. In no case, for example, was it possible to portray fully the background and history of a contribution, or, for that matter, to give as much attention to its current development as we would have liked. Also, we have attempted to write where possible with the layman in mind.

In preparing this volume we consulted many of the experts and leading investigators on the various individual subjects. Each and all have been most generous in talking and writing to us and in reviewing and commenting on our first efforts. The names of those who have been consulted at various times are listed in the back of this book. It needs hardly to be added that, despite this imposing list of generous helpers, responsibility for any errors made or other defects is entirely that of the authors.

We should, in addition, make special mention of some people who worked directly with us. These include Miss Janice DeMoor who carried a great load in gathering material and in assisting in the writing of Chapters 1, 2, and 3; and Messrs. Alf Christoffersen, Ellis Myers, and Robert Walton, who collected and helped choose many of the photographs; and Mrs. Hazel Williams, Mrs. Pennijean Savage, Mrs. Shirley Sheckels, and Mrs. Carol Wicks, who cheerfully and efficiently typed and retyped the manuscript in its several evolutions. We also wish to express our gratitude to the United States Atomic Energy Commission for having afforded us this opportunity to review an important and truly fascinating field of scientific and technological advance.

There is one other spirit which breathes in these pages. It belongs to Charter Heslep, originally designated as one of the authors of the book, who died in September 1963 while travelling in its behalf. Charter left behind, as an inspiration to us all, the memory of his great gifts, as well as of his warm personality and his matchless enthusiasm, energy and devotion.

J. H. L.
B. M.
B. S. L.

Introduction

Radioisotopes are unstable isotopes of the elements. They decay by the emission of radiation. Generally, radioisotopes can be used in two ways—as tracers, or as sources of radiation. They may be used as tracers because of two important properties—first, their chemical behavior is identical with that of stable isotopes of the same elements; second, they decay by the emission of radiation which can be detected so as to indicate their position and quantity. As radiation sources radioisotopes find application either by being detectable after having been absorbed or scattered by matter or by forming excited molecular species or ions and thus initiating chemical or biological reactions.

Tracer applications (in diagnosis and research) are by far the most important uses of radioisotopes in medicine at this time and perhaps also in agriculture and industry. They are also the most familiar, however, and consequently this introductory discussion will have to do primarily with some technical aspects of the uses of radioisotopes as sources of radiation.

Radioisotope radiations occur in the form either of high energy particles (alpha particles and beta rays) or of electromagnetic waves (gamma rays). Gamma rays penetrate deeply into matter, whereas beta rays and alpha particles are capable only of shallow penetration. All can penetrate liquids and solids which are opaque to visible light.

At sufficient intensities radioisotope radiations can initiate chemical and biological reactions. They do this without significantly raising the temperature of the absorbing medium if the field intensity, target thermal conductivity and thickness, and periods of exposure are held to reasonable limits. They do it without making the absorbing medium radioactive

Twelve tanks for storage of high level radioactive wastes are shown during construction at the USAEC's Hanford Atomic Products Operation, Richland, Washington. This "tank farm" is one of several located near the Hanford chemical separations plants from which the wastes come. The tanks are already being "mined" for their valuable store of radioisotopes.

if radiation energy, field intensity, and target composition are kept within certain limits.

Radiations can also be produced by a variety of machines. Certain of these, such as Van de Graaff generators, produce fast electrons having penetrating ability similar to that of beta rays. In other machines, such as linear accelerators and cyclotrons, electrons can be accelerated to much higher energies than those available from radioisotope beta rays, and heavy ions can be accelerated to much higher energies than those available from radioisotope alpha particles. Machines can also be converted to Bremstrahlung or gamma-ray-producing devices. In short, for practically every use of a radioisotope as a radiation source, a machine can also be substituted. The choice between a radioisotope or a machine for a particular application will generally be based on the relative economics, convenience, and reliability of the two alternatives.

Radioisotopes can be produced on a practical scale by neutron irradiation, by recovery from fission wastes, or by bombardment of target materials by charged particles in cyclotrons. There is a tremendous capacity in the United States for production by reactors. Huge amounts of cesium 137, strontium 90, promethium 147, and other fission products are present in fission wastes at the United States Atomic Energy Commission's fissionable materials production sites and the Commission has announced that megacurie amounts of a variety of radioisotopes are now available for purchase at Hanford. In addition, almost unlimited amounts of cobalt 60 could be produced by conversion of the USAEC's production reactors. A beginning in this direction has been made at Savannah River where reactors have been made available for the production of megacurie amounts of cobalt 60. The prices charged for fission-produced radioisotopes have decreased sharply from what they were several years ago, and further price declines are in prospect.

During 1962 the USAEC made two significant steps to broaden the base of isotope technology. One was the construction of an Isotopes Development Center at Oak Ridge National

Container used for shipping large quantities of fission products.

Exterior view of one of the five nuclear reactors which produce fissionable plutonium at the USAEC's Savannah River Plant, Aiken, South Carolina. Megacurie amounts of cobalt 60 have also been produced in one of these reactors.

Laboratory; the other the establishment of a High Intensity Radiation Development Laboratory (HIRDL) at Brookhaven National Laboratory. The major concern at the Oak Ridge Center is with fission products. Methods are being developed for purifying the main long-lived fission products— cesium 137, strontium 90, cerium 144, and promethium 147—and for converting them into useful chemical compounds and physical forms. The chemical, physical, and radiation properties of these and other fission products in all their possible forms are being investigated in detail. In addition, methods for separating fission products from waste streams are being developed, principal emphasis being placed on solvent extraction processes.

Along with the relatively new work on fission products, ORNL is continuing its traditional research on radioisotopes produced by neutron irradiation of stable isotopes. Processes for producing most of the well-known radioisotopes— iodine 131, phosphorus 32, carbon 14, sulfur 35, etc.—were developed at ORNL and a continuing effort has been made to improve these processes and the quality of the products obtained from them.

There are several cyclotrons in the United States producing radioactive isotopes which either could not be produced by reactors or would be produced less efficiently by reactors. Among these are the 144-inch cyclotron at the Carnegie Institute of Technology in Pittsburgh, the 88-inch cyclotron in Berkeley, and finally the 85-inch proton cyclotron at the new ORNL center which has the largest beam current of any in the world. The latter is a major factor in the production of neutron-deficient radioisotopes.

Before the ability of intense radiation fields to initiate chemical or biological reactions is adopted for any commercial purpose, it is necessary that there be a precise evaluation of certain factors. These include the uniformity with which the target material will receive radiation, the availability of reliable techniques for fabricating the radiation source, and the availability of reliable irradiator equipment. The HIRDL facility at Brookhaven provides the means for doing research and development work relating to these

and other aspects of high intensity radiation technology. It contains two cells, each able to handle megacurie amounts of radioisotopes. As of early 1964 there were approximately 600 kilocuries of cobalt 60 and 200 kilocuries of cesium 137 on hand.

In addition to these government facilities, there are a wide variety of commercial radioisotope facilities and services available in the United States. Similarly, a large variety of radiation-producing machines have been commercially developed. These range from cyclotrons and betatrons to Van de Graaff generators, resonant transformers, and linear accelerators. Many of these devices are being used for analytical and production purposes.

Remote controls used to operate facilities for production of radioisotopes at the Isotopes Development Center, Oak Ridge National Laboratory.

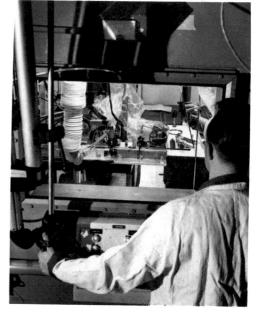

View through window of preparation cell at High Intensity Radiation Development Laboratory, Brookhaven National Laboratory, during encapsulation of cobalt 60 radiation sources.

Chapter 1
Medical Diagnosis and Research

Medical Diagnosis and Research

When cyclotrons were first developed during the period from 1929 to 1935, the first artificially produced radioactive isotopes became available. Almost immediately thereafter, these isotopes were provided for investigators in medical centers throughout the United States as well as in many other countries. During this early period scientists from the United States assisted in designing cyclotrons which were built in several countries for experimental work in physics, radiochemistry, biology and medicine. After 1945, with the development of nuclear reactors, larger quantities and varieties of radioactive isotopes became available. In more recent years, many pharmaceutical and other companies in the United States and abroad have undertaken the preparation of isotopically-labeled products. Today reactor-produced and cyclotron-produced isotopes are available almost everywhere in the United States, and diverse compounds containing them have been furnished widely to investigators for research, diagnostic and therapeutic purposes. The extensive scope of the application of atomic energy products to biological, medical and environmental research in the United States may readily be seen from the fact that over 70 million dollars were available for these purposes from the Atomic Energy Commission in the year beginning July 1, 1963.

The most important medical use of these radioactive isotopes has been as tracers of metabolic processes. They have been used, for example, to measure the amount and the movement in the body of water, electrolytes, fats, proteins, hormones, and other important substances. For these studies the appropriate molecule is labeled with a radioactive isotope. The labeled compound is injected or ingested, and the radioactivity and the chemical composition may then be measured serially in the blood, urine, or other body fluids. The curve obtained by graphing these data may be analyzed to determine the amounts of the substance in various compartments of the body and the rates at which the substance enters and leaves these compartments. The results are often analyzed in combination with in-vivo counting data. Detailed information concerning the complex interrelationship of biochemical pathways is obtained, and this may be used to quantitate the dynamics of human metabolism. Many such studies have led to diagnostic tests and applications.

In the pages that follow we describe some examples of relatively recent diagnostic and research studies of the types noted above.

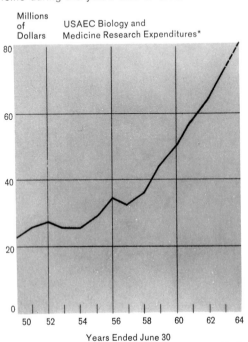

Graph showing increase in money expended by the U.S.A.E.C. for research in Biology and Medicine during the years 1950 to 1964.

Millions of Dollars — USAEC Biology and Medicine Research Expenditures*

Years Ended June 30
*Plant included on an obligations basis all other items on a cost basis

Metabolic Studies with Carbon 14 Compounds

Many carbon compounds of metabolic interest, such as sugars, fats, and amino acids, are oxidized in the body to carbon dioxide, which then appears in the expired air. The study of the metabolic processes involved has led to the development of breath analyzing devices which are of great value in medical research, and in some instances in diagnosis. A tracer dose of a specific carbon-14-labeled compound is first administered. A specially designed plastic helmet is then placed over the subject's head to collect all the expired air, which is then monitored both for total carbon dioxide content and for total radioactive carbon dioxide content. Simultaneously, the subject's total intake and output of carbon dioxide and oxygen are determined. From this information it is possible to determine the specific activity of the $C^{14}O_2$ (radioactivity per given amount of CO_2) in the expired breath. Thus the total fraction of eliminated labeled carbon and the rate of its oxidation to $C^{14}O_2$ can be determined. Since total oxygen consumption is also measured, the respiratory quotient (CO_2/O_2), important in metabolic studies, may be derived simultaneously.

The uses of breath analyzers are based on the fact that in the healthy person there is a characteristic pattern of $C^{14}O_2$ elimination for a given metabolite. If deviations from this normal pattern are studied and quantitated, valuable information may be obtained for the understanding of certain types of obesity; of metabolic diseases such as diabetes, acromegaly, gout, and anemia; and of many other conditions.

Differentiating Anemia
An example of the use of breath analyzers is a recent study of the metabolism of carbon-14-labeled histidine, an amino acid, in normal subjects and in patients with megaloblastic anemia. This condition can be caused by a deficiency in either vitamin-B_{12} or folic acid. Important differences in expired $C^{14}O_2$ were discovered by which the two types of cases could be distinguished in a one-hour test. In cases caused by folic acid deficiency there was

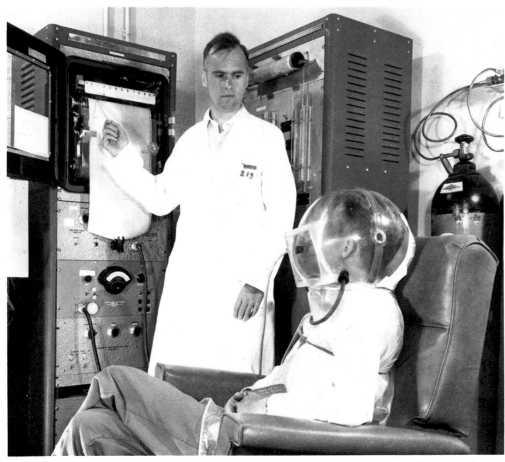

A carbon-14 breath analyzer. The expired air is collected and monitored for carbon-14 content. This leads to continuous, automatic recording of the total intake and output of carbon dioxide and oxygen, as well as of the carbon-14 activity.

$C^{14}O_2$ specific activity, $\mu c/g$ carbon/10 μc injected

Vitamin B_{12} deficient (C.K. ♂ 86)

Normal subject (C-1)

Folic acid deficient (R.M. ♀ 30)

Minutes

This shows the carbon-14-specific activity curves for a normal subject, a patient with vitamin B_{12}-deficiency anemia, and a patient with folic acid-deficiency anemia after intravenous administration of 0.5 mg. L-histidine-2(ring)-carbon 14 (approximately 25 microcuries.) Note that the patterns for both the normal subject and the vitamin B_{12}-deficient patient show a rapid rise to a maximum in about 40 minutes and a gradual decline, whereas that for the folic acid-deficient patient shows a slow rise and a relatively low and delayed maximum at 4 hours.

both a marked diminution in the amount of $C^{14}O_2$ expired and a delay in the appearance of maximum $C^{14}O_2$ specific activity, whereas in cases caused by vitamin-B_{12} deficiency both of these parameters were normal. These findings are explained by the fact that in folic acid deficiency there is a defect in the metabolic pathway which normally allows the CO_2 to be produced, since folic acid plays an essential role as acceptor of the single carbon moiety from histidine or other donors and as the sole means for transferring it to other important reactions. In cases of vitamin-B_{12} deficiency, i.e., pernicious anemia, there is no such defect and the CO_2 production is normal.

Glucose Metabolism

In some studies breath analyzers are used in conjunction with repeated analyses of the blood, urine or feces. An example is the study of the relationship of glucose oxidation to obesity performed by Pollycove at Donner Laboratory (University of California, Berkeley). He administered carbon-14-labeled glucose to subjects and studied its metabolism in the body. The carbon 14 breath analyzer was used to measure the specific activity of $C^{14}O_2$ in the expired air, and serial blood samples were analyzed to determine the size of the glucose pool in the body and the glucose turnover rate. The glucose pool and glucose turnover rates proved to be the same for normal and obese subjects, but glucose oxidation was markedly diminished in some obese subjects. These results indicated that certain forms of obesity may be related to an inability to oxidize glucose normally, and that in these cases glucose may be converted to fat at an abnormal rate.

A related study of energy metabolism was later conducted by Gordon and associates at the University of Wisconsin Medical School. With the breath analyzer they measured the $C^{14}O_2$ in expired air following administration of carbon-14-labeled glucose and certain fatty acids. They also analyzed blood samples for specific activity of carbon 14. They found that in one type of obesity there is a decreased oxidation of glucose which responds to the administration of thyroid hormone. They also demonstrated that short-chain fatty acids were oxidized to

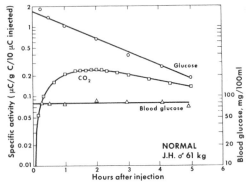

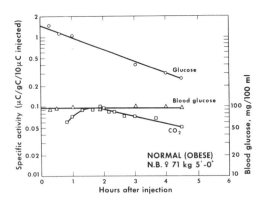

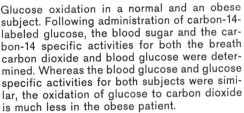

Glucose oxidation in a normal and an obese subject. Following administration of carbon-14-labeled glucose, the blood sugar and the carbon-14 specific activities for both the breath carbon dioxide and blood glucose were determined. Whereas the blood glucose and glucose specific activities for both subjects were similar, the oxidation of glucose to carbon dioxide is much less in the obese patient.

Curves for diabetic patient demonstrating the increase in glucose oxidation and lowering of blood glucose level when patient was controlled with insulin.

CO_2 and water at a significantly subnormal rate in these obese subjects, whereas the turnover rate of the fatty acid in the body was the same as that for normal subjects. They concluded that the fatty acids were probably stored as fat.

Additional studies using breath analysis in combination with serial blood analysis were concerned with the mechanism of insulin action in normal subjects. These studies confirmed that insulin not only increases the oxidation of glucose to CO_2 and water but also simultaneously inhibits the breakdown of glycogen to glucose. These results indicate that the precipitous fall in blood glucose observed when insulin is administered is caused by a combination of the two effects. Other studies showed the action of tolbutamide, an oral agent used to control diabetes. The effects were delayed because they depend upon stimulation of pancreatic secretion of insulin. In other studies of diabetic patients the abnormal curves returned to normal when the patients were controlled with insulin. Patients with acromegaly who had associated diabetes showed a diabetic type of glucose oxidation, but after treatment with heavy particle irradiation to the pituitary their glucose oxidation returned to normal.

Enzyme Systems

Scientists at Argonne Cancer Research Hospital have used their carbon 14 breath analyzer to study certain enzyme systems. The pattern of appearance of the labeled carbon dioxide in the expired air may reflect the pathway of utilization followed by an administered labeled substance, and this pathway is in turn determined by the enzyme system involved. Thus diseases which alter specific enzyme systems, or congenital deficiencies of enzyme systems, can be detected by administering a carbon-14-labeled substrate and determining its pattern of oxidation. One study, for example, has demonstrated aberration of metabolism in individuals with a congenital lack of the enzyme glucose-6-phosphate dehydrogenase. Informative studies have also been performed, using the appropriate carbon-14-labeled compound on gout, hyperlipemia, diabetes, and selected forms of cancer. In addition, this approach has been used to determine the mechanism

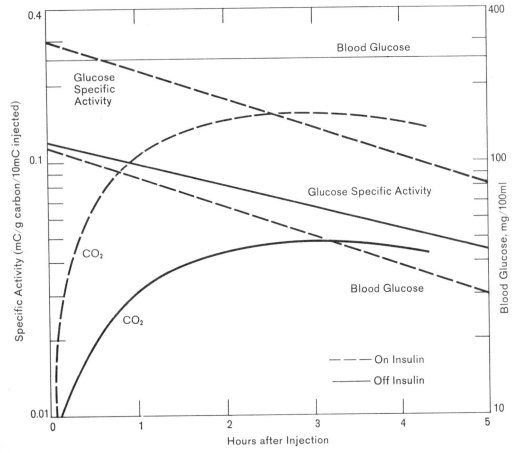

of action of certain hormones. For example, recent studies indicate that the parathyroid hormones modify human citrate metabolism.

Hematology

Some of the most important advances in the field of hematology (the study of blood and blood-forming organs) during recent years have been accomplished with the aid of radioisotopes. These include studies of the kinetics of iron metabolism and the rates of production and destruction of red cells, especially with the aid of iron 59; studies of the life span of red blood cells with chromium 51 and of red cells, white cells and platelets with diisopropylfluorophosphate (DFP-32); and studies of the developing red blood cells, white blood cells, and platelets with tritium-labeled thymidine. Based on these studies, a wide variety of radioisotope procedures are now used in assessing various blood disorders. Finally, there has been considerable advance in the understanding of the control of red cell production from the research on erythropoietin.

Blood Cell Studies

The injection of DFP-32 results in the labeling of red blood cells, white blood cells, and platelets, and thus the survival of these three important circulating elements may be determined by separating them in the blood samples taken. Athens and his colleagues at the University of Utah Medical School have shown by using DFP-32-labeled white cells that the granulocytes (one of the types of white blood cells) are normally removed from the circulation with a half-time of seven hours, and also that approximately half of the granulocytes within the blood vessels cling to the vessel walls. A more rapid removal of granulocytes from the blood and migration into the tissues has been observed in patients with infections.

One of the earliest methods for detecting ionizing radiation was by the use of photographic emulsion for the development of autoradiographs. With new types of photographic emulsions developed in recent years radioisotopes within individual cells and, in some cases, within parts of cells can be detected. The resolution which can be obtained is dependent on the energy of the radiation emitted by the radioactive isotope. Tritium is one of the best isotopes from the resolution viewpoint, and it can

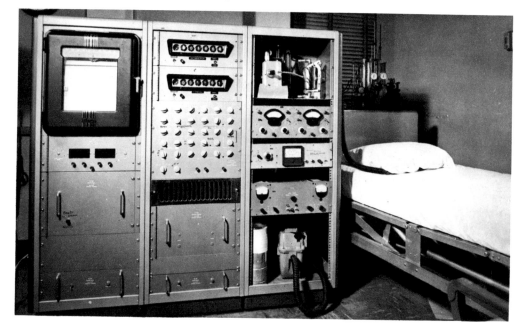

Argonne Cancer Research Hospital Continuous $C^{14}O_2$ Monitor and Data Logging System. The central third of the console contains the data-logging and data-processing unit. Pertinent variables (counter efficiency, dose, barometric pressure, temperature, etc.) can be introduced into the computer system by appropriate setting of the dials. Expired air is collected by a face mask, and the unit operates as a closed system.

be rather easily substituted in molecules of biological interest. Two of the most important of these are deoxyribonucleic acid (DNA), which carries genetic information from generation to generation of cells, and ribonucleic acid (RNA), which transfers this information to and processes it in the synthetic apparatus of the cell. The availability of tritium-labeled precursors for DNA and RNA, as well as for various amino acids, has provided a very potent tool for hematological studies, making possible, for example, the study of various biochemical events in individual cells of hematopoietic tissue. It is most fortunate that this methodology has become available since the diffuse nature of hematopoietic tissue and the variety of cell types found in it limit the usefulness of most biochemical methods.

Considerable information on the growth of cells in hematopoietic tissue has been obtained by following the changes in the labeling pattern of cells in various stages of maturation after the injection of the specific DNA precursor, tritiated thymidine. This substance is rapidly removed from the blood and incorporated into the DNA of cell nuclei. After cell division each cell nucleus contains half of the labeled DNA of the parent cell. Analysis of these labeling patterns has provided information regarding the life spans, the time spent at various stages of maturation, and the ultimate fate of the different hematopoietic tissues. One illustration of the changes in our knowledge of hematopoietic tissue which has resulted primarily from such auto-radiographic studies is the newer knowledge of the life history of the lymphocyte. Only a few years ago the lymphocyte was thought to be a relatively short-lived cell. Now it is believed to have a life span of at least 100 days. This knowledge has required reevaluation of the physiological significance of the lymphocyte. The autoradiographic method has also provided much information on mechanisms of chromosomal replication and on the proliferation of cells in many of the body tissues. Investigators at Brookhaven and elsewhere have used tritiated thymidine to study the rates at which immature human blood cells grow.

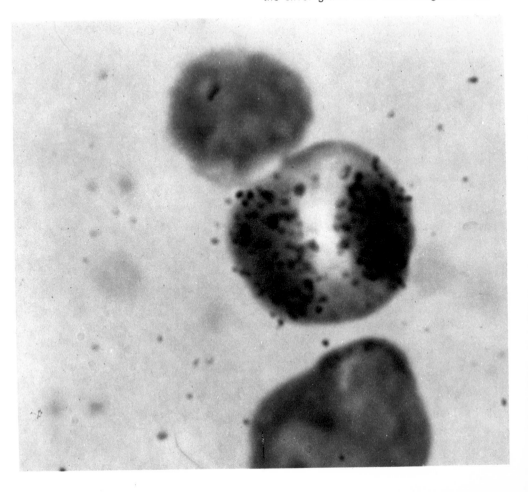

Radioautograph of bone marrow cell that is just about to complete its division into two cells. The granules of silver seen over the cells are caused by the action of the beta radiation emitted by the tritium-labeled thymidine on the photographic emulsion which lies immediately over the cells. Note the equal distribution of the silver grains over each daughter nucleus.

Iron Kinetic Studies

When scintillation counters became available, it became possible to study the kinetics of metabolic processes in the body. For example, with *in-vivo* scintillation counters (i.e., counters placed over various organs of the body) the movement and quantitation of labeled materials could now be evaluated both from the radioactivity in samples of blood, urine, and other tissues, and from the radioactivity in various organs. The first such studies in humans were carried out in 1947, using iron 59 to study iron metabolism in normal and pathologic states. Today iron 59 studies are routine diagnostic procedures in studying obscure anemias and other blood disorders.

The information obtained in these studies can be used to set up mathematical models which quantitate the movement of iron within the body. The study of such models has helped in understanding iron metabolism in health and disease. For example, if radioiron is administered to a normal subject the plasma concentration will fall exponentially and slowly level off after two weeks because of normal feedback from storage reserve iron. Therefore, if a patient is given radioiron and the plasma concentration is observed to fall more rapidly and to level off much sooner, one can suspect feedback of iron from some other source. This is often due to the presence of a hemolytic process, the abnormally rapid breakdown of red cells resulting in the release of iron.

Whether or not the spleen is implicated in such an excessive destruction of red blood cells may also be easily detected by placing the scintillation counter over the spleen. A rapid rise in iron 59 activity indicates active production of red blood cells whereas, if the count rises less rapidly but remains high, excessive splenic sequestration and destruction of red cells are present. In acquired hemolytic anemia the red blood cell production may be increased tenfold, but this is not enough to compensate for a twentyfold reduction of mean red blood cell life span associated with destruction of red blood cells by the spleen. This type of anemia is often successfully treated by surgical removal of the spleen.

Locating the site of red cell production and destruction, such as can be done

The multiple-port *in vivo* scintillation counter is used for iron kinetic studies. The tracer dose of iron 59 is administered into the arm vein and then the activities in the bone marrow, liver, and spleen are recorded simultaneously with counters positioned over these areas. Counts are made periodically over a two-week period. Graphs obtained from these data show the distribution of the iron 59 at these sites as a function of time. When analyzed in conjunction with iron-59 content in blood samples, one can obtain information concerning the sites of red blood cell production and destruction in the body.

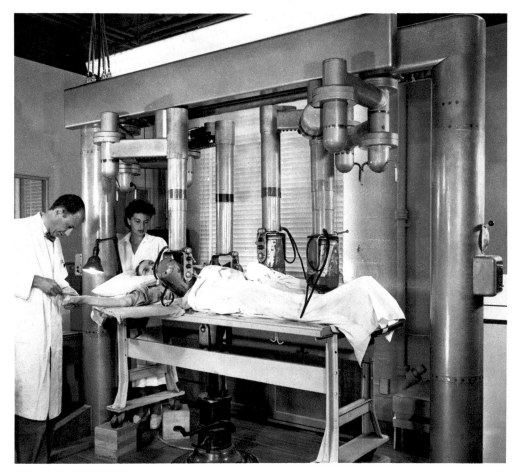

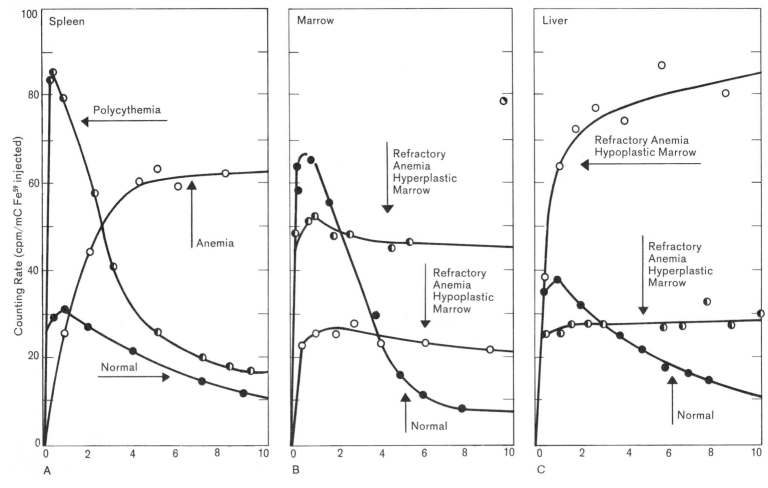

In-vivo iron-59 studies showing the activity over the spleen, bone marrow, and liver of a normal subject and how these curves vary in patients with different blood disorders.

A) The patient with polycythemia, in this case, shows an abnormally rapid rise in iron-59 activity indicating red blood cell production by the spleen. The patient with anemia shows a slower rise, but the curve remains abnormally high indicating sequestration and destruction of red blood cells by the spleen.

B) Two patients with refractory anemia are compared. The one with hyperplastic marrow shows a rapid uptake of the iron by the marrow (rapid production of red cells); the curve remains high indicating abnormal destruction of developing red cells and iron re-utilization. The one with hypoplastic marrow indicates poor uptake of the radioiron, the bone marrow not producing red cells at a normal rate.

C) Two patients with refractory anemia are compared. In the case of the patient with hypoplastic marrow (see B) the liver curve is abnormally high indicating that the radioiron has gone to the liver instead of to the marrow.

Normal iron kinetics model. The plasma iron goes mainly to the bone marrow where it is incorporated into the developing red blood cells (erythrons). These subsequently appear as circulating red blood cells (erythrocytes), which contain most of the body's iron. Some of the plasma iron goes into storage, and this iron is available to the body when needed.

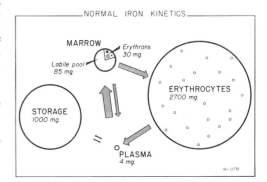

NORMAL IRON KINETICS

with iron kinetic studies, is often of value in understanding disease mechanisms. In pernicious anemia, for example, the abnormal destruction of developing red blood cells in the bone marrow can be observed with the scintillation counter directed at a large volume of marrow, such as the bony pelvis. This finding is in accord with the known impairment of red cell maturation resulting from vitamin B_{12} deficiency.

Erythropoietin

Iron, contained in hemoglobin, is incorporated into the red blood cell during its developmental stages in the bone marrow and stays in the cell until it dies. The percentage uptake of tracer iron in red cells provides the basis for measuring red blood cell production and is a sensitive indicator for determining the influence of various factors on red cell production rates. One outstanding result has been the demonstration that red blood cell formation, like endocrine organs such as the thyroid and adrenals, is controlled by a hormone carried in the circulation. With the use of the radioactive iron uptake test in animals, the concentration in body fluids of this red cell stimulating hormone, erythropoietin, can be measured. The amount of erythropoietin has been related to abnormalities in blood counts. For example, the very high red cell counts (polycythemia) associated with residence at high altitude have been correlated with elevated concentrations of erythropoietin.

In addition to being responsible for increased red cell numbers in these abnormal situations, erythropoietin is responsible for the fine regulation of the normal concentration of red cells in the blood. At the University of California Schooley has shown that if erythropoietin antibodies are given to normal animals red cell production ceases and the incorporation of radio-iron into red cells is essentially zero. Conversely, a chronic increase in erythropoietin concentration in the circulation results in an increase of the red bone marrow with extension into bones which normally would contain only fatty marrow; in some cases there is extension into sites outside the bones such as the spleen.

A recently perfected technique utilizes the short-lived positron-emitting isotope

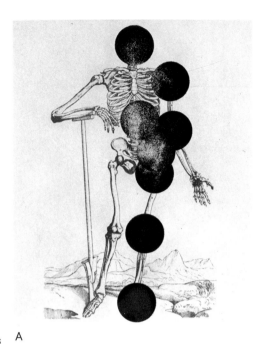

A

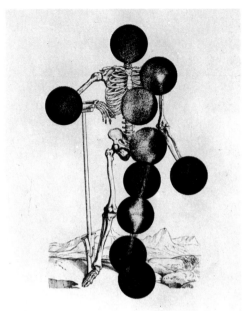

B

C

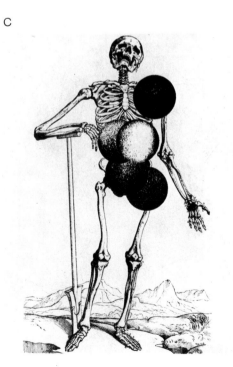

Selected areas from iron-52 scans superimposed on skeletons showing bone marrow activity (production of red blood cells) in various parts of the body in different subjects.

A) Distribution of marrow in normal adult. There is essentially no active marrow in the arms or legs.

B) Distribution of marrow in patient with chronically elevated erythropoietin concentration in his blood resulting from severe cyanotic congenital heart disease with a marked increase in red blood cell count. The red cell producing marrow can be seen in the bones of the arms and legs, particularly the knee.

C) Patient with an elevated erythropoietin concentration in the blood associated with severe anemia. The red cell producing marrow had left the skeleton entirely and had migrated to the spleen. This illustrates the fact that factors other than erythropoietin play a determining role in red cell production.

iron 52, and the positron scintillation camera for visualizing the distribution of marrow in the body. The illustration shows a series of studies which demonstrate the normal marrow distribution and the changes in this distribution which accompany certain diseases. Multiple views taken with the positron scintillation camera 15 hours after administration of a tracer dose of iron 52, produced for the purpose in the Berkeley 88-inch cyclotron, have been superimposed on a drawing of the skeleton for orientation. As can be seen there is essentially no red marrow in the arms and legs of the normal subject. The distribution of marrow is quite different in a man with chronically elevated erythropoietin concentration in his blood. In a patient having congenital heart disease with severe cynosis a marked increase in red cell producing marrow is present in the bones of both the arms and the legs, resulting in an increase in the count of red blood cells. In another patient, who has an elevated erythropoietic hormone concentration in the blood associated with severe anemia, the red cell producing marrow has left the skeleton entirely and migrated to the spleen. This patient illustrates the fact that factors other than a red cell stimulating hormone play a determining role in red cell production. The exact nature of all the factors involved is, as yet, unknown.

The amount of erythropoietin necessary to increase red cell production in the normal human being has been determined. Although some anemic patients have elevated concentrations of erythropoietin, it is reasonable to assume that a deficiency in production of this hormone may be the cause of the anemia in a fair percentage of cases. Evaluation of the usefulness of this hormone in the treatment of human disease must await the development of assay methods sufficiently sensitive to demonstrate deficiencies, and of methods of obtaining sufficient quantities of the hormone for diagnostic or therapeutic purposes.

Organ Function Studies

Cardiac Output

It is important to know the amount of blood pumped by the heart per minute because this is a measure of the effectiveness of the heart in circulating the blood. The first accurate method for measuring cardiac output required that catheters be inserted into both the right heart and an artery in order to determine the difference in oxygen concentrations of the blood entering and leaving the heart. By using the Fick principle, this oxygen difference was related to the oxygen consumption (measured by breath analysis), and thus the amount of blood pumped by the heart each minute was determined. Hamilton, at the University of Georgia, demonstrated that it was only necessary to catheterize the artery and then to use the wave of appearance and disappearance of an injected dye in the arterial blood to determine cardiac output. When radioactive isotopes became available they replaced the dye as a tracer in this technique because they could be measured more easily and accurately. Huff and colleagues demonstrated in 1955 a technique whereby cardiac output could be determined by the external measurement of blood radioactivity with a scintillation probe placed over the heart, thus obviating the need for arterial catheterization. Since that time this technique has become refined and standardized so that today its results are comparable to those obtained by an indwelling arterial needle or catheter. The determination of cardiac output is now an accurate and simple procedure for assessing the function of the heart. It is important in treating patients with various heart diseases. It has also helped in our understanding of certain other diseases. For example, patients with polycythemia vera have increased blood volumes and it was thought that the cardiac output increased proportionately. Studies have shown, however, that although the cardiac output is usually increased somewhat in some such patients, the increase is not sufficiently great to maintain the normal movement of the blood through the body.

Recently attempts have been made to quantitate the coronary blood flow (the blood supply to the heart muscle) with

Subject in position for a cardiac output study. The probe is positioned over the heart and the passage of RISA through this area is recorded.

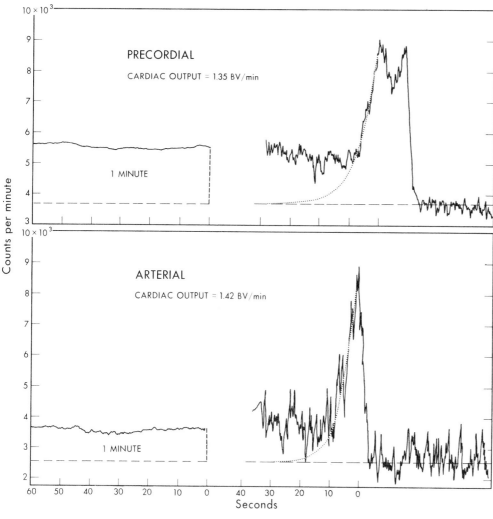

PRECORDIAL

CARDIAC OUTPUT = 1.35 BV/min

1 MINUTE

ARTERIAL

CARDIAC OUTPUT = 1.42 BV/min

1 MINUTE

Counts per minute

Seconds

These graphs show the results of coronary blood flow studies performed on a normal subject and a patient with coronary disease.
Top: In the normal subject there is a relative prolongation of the left heart downslope indicating that there is no obstruction of the main branches of the coronary arteries.
Bottom: In the patient with coronary disease the heart and brain downslopes are similar. The relative lack of prolongation of the left heart downslope, compared to normal subjects, is evidence of interference in the coronary blood flow.

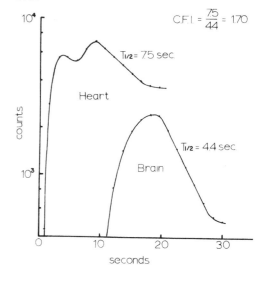

$$C.F.I. = \frac{75}{44} = 1.70$$

Heart

$T_{1/2} = 75$ sec

Brain

$T_{1/2} = 44$ sec

counts

seconds

Comparison of curves shows that the cardiac output determined by the external monitoring of an injected radioisotope (top) is comparable to that based on serial blood samples taken by means of an in-dwelling arterial needle.

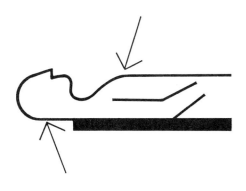

Positioning of the scintillation detectors over the left heart and the occipital region of the brain for performing a coronary blood flow study.

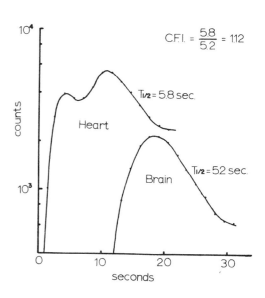

$$C.F.I. = \frac{5.8}{5.2} = 1.12$$

Heart

$T_{1/2} = 5.8$ sec.

Brain

$T_{1/2} = 52$ sec.

counts

seconds

similar external measuring techniques. Such determinations can be of value in detecting coronary disease. Difficulties in measuring this very small fraction of the total output of the heart are still being worked out.

Kidney Function

When iodine-131-Hippuran is administered to a patient, and the counting rates recorded by probes placed over each kidney, a graph, called a renogram, can be obtained by plotting these counting rates as a function of time. This technique, introduced in 1956 by Taplin and associates at the University of California at Los Angeles, has been very helpful in studying kidney function. For example, it can be used to diagnose unilateral renal ischemia (a reduction of blood supply to one kidney) which is one cause of high blood pressure that can be corrected by surgery.

The iodine-131-Hippuran renogram also makes possible other measurements of renal blood flow. The differential blood flow between kidneys is determined by comparing the slopes of the renogram's first segments, which are indices of relative renal plasma or blood flow. If the right kidney slope is 3 times that of the left kidney, then the proportion of blood flowing to the right compared to the left kidney is 3:1. If the total flow to both kidneys is known (this may be determined from the percent of radiohippuran excreted in 15 minutes) it is possible to quantitate the blood flow to each kidney.

The renocystogram employs three probes—the two kidney probes and an additional one over the bladder. Thus it is also possible to measure the continuous combined kidney excretion and the residual urine volume in the bladder after voiding.

Renograms and renocystograms are of particular value in providing a means for studying pyelonephritis (inflammation of the kidney) without cystoscopy and bilateral ureteral catheterization, procedures which may themselves introduce infection. They can also demonstrate slight differences in function between kidneys which would not be discernible as differences in radiopacity in an intravenous pyelogram. Such studies cannot entirely replace pyelography because they usually do not detect structural lesions of the

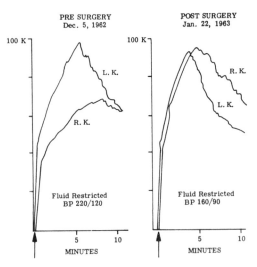

RENAL ARTERY OCCLUSIVE DISEASE

PRE SURGERY Dec. 5, 1962

POST SURGERY Jan. 22, 1963

Fluid Restricted BP 220/120

Fluid Restricted BP 160/90

Renograms made before and after surgery in a patient with high blood pressure due to renal artery occlusive disease. The curve for the right kidney (R.K.) which was much lower before surgery became like that for the left kidney after surgery. The blood pressure prior to surgery was elevated (220/120); following surgery it had dropped to 160/90.

A patient seated in a specially designed chair with the three scintillation detectors in proper position for obtaining the iodine-131-labeled Hippuran renocystogram. One detector is aimed at each kidney, and a third at the bladder area.

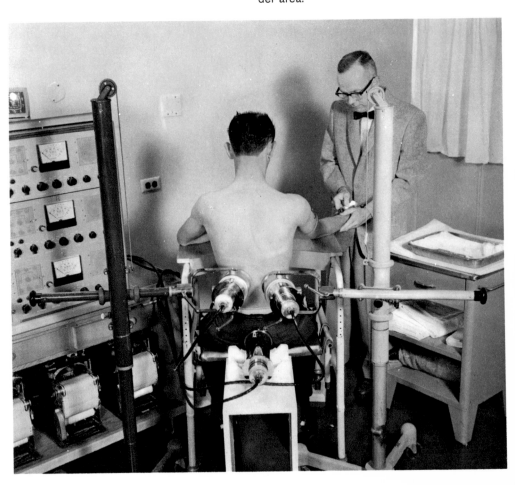

urinary tract. They are of value in correctly analyzing the pyelogram, however, and when both the renogram and the pyelogram are employed, diagnostic accuracy is increased.

Liver Function
Iodine-131-labeled Rose Bengal is an agent employed in making a hepatogram, useful in studying liver function and liver blood flow. The methods for making and using hepatograms are quite similar to those for renograms as described above, and there are many useful diagnostic and research applications in health and in abnormal states.

Positioning of the three scintillation detectors and arrangement of equipment for obtaining the iodine-131-labeled Rose Bengal hepatogram which measures the rates of dye disappearance from the blood, its accumulation in and excretion from the liver, and its appearance in the upper intestine.

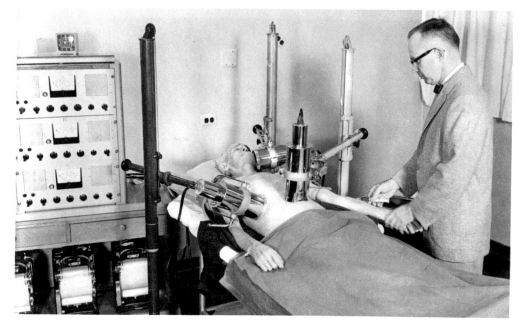

Visualizing or Measuring Labeled Compounds in the Living Body

In 1936 thyroid iodine uptake studies were performed by administering a small amount of cyclotron-produced radioactive iodine to a subject, and then holding a Geiger counter tube directly over the thyroid gland to detect the location of the isotope. The basic principle for studying iodine uptake remains unchanged, but improvements in instrumentation were brought about during the early 1950's with the introduction of various types of scintillation counters, requiring much smaller tracer doses. Later came the development of radioisotope scanners and cameras, highly developed electronic devices which enable the physician to visualize the distribution of radioactive substances within the living body, thereby assessing the size, shape, position, and function of organs, and locating lesions therein.

Development of Scanners
Different types of scanners vary in their construction and operation. Basically, however, they are alike in the employment of certain essential parts: a gamma detector; a collimating system; electronic amplification, discrimination, and counting-rate determination; and some means of visual representation.

The first instrument designed for isotope scanning was the dot scanner, developed in 1950 independently by Cassen at the University of California at Los Angeles and Mayneord at the Royal Cancer Hospital in London. A collimated scintillation counter detected the radiation, and the counts were then recorded by means of a tapper bar making corresponding points on a piece of paper. The number of dots recorded in a given area was proportional to the amount of activity detected.

The early dot scanner did not contain any means for screening out low-energy scattered, or background, radiation. It was successful for thyroid scanning because the thyroid gland lies just beneath the skin surface so that scattering is minimal. Before scanning techniques could be applied successfully to organs which lie deeper, improvements in instrumentation to deal with this problem of scatter were needed.

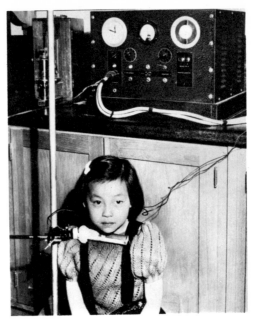

One of the first iodine uptake studies in progress. The radioiodine, prepared by bombarding tellurium with deuterons from a cyclotron, consisted mainly of iodine 131 but also contained small amounts of iodine 124 and iodine 126. After oral administration, the radioactivity in the thyroid gland was counted by a Geiger counter tube placed directly over the thyroid.

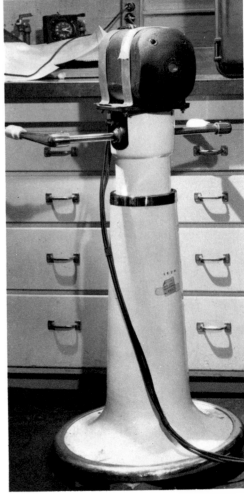

An early *in vivo* scintillation counter head. It could be positioned over various areas of the body to detect radioactivity in an organ.

The first well-type scintillation counter used in 1950. Samples of blood or other material were placed in the counter. Emitted gamma rays were detected and counted by a sodium iodide scintillation crystal.

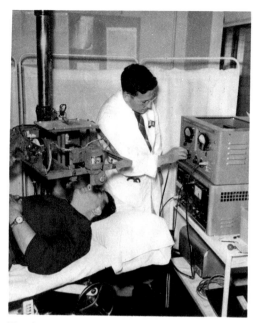

The first dot scanner. It was designed in 1950 by Cassen at the University of California at Los Angeles.

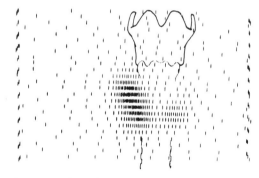

A scan made with the first dot scanner showing uptake of iodine 131 in a patient who seven years before had a partial thyroidectomy on the left side. Note greater uptake by right thyroid (left side of picture) and partial uptake by remaining tissue on left thyroid.

The first such improvement was pulse-height selection. By this method it was possible electronically to select the energy corresponding to that of the emitted gamma ray (known as the photopeak region), to reject the lower energy scattered radiation, and thus to produce a dot-scan which more accurately pictured the isotope distribution.

A focusing collimator (one with several channels which can be directed at a point several centimeters from the front face) was subsequently designed. For a given radioisotope dosage, this device improved the resolution of scans by narrowing the area "seen" by the crystal, thus increasing the proportion of gamma rays which reached the crystal from the point of interest. In addition, "background erase" was introduced, a technique which prevented the tapper bar from recording dots unless a certain minimum counting rate was detected. This improved the contrast, hence the interpretability, of the picture.

The photoscanner, developed in 1954 by Kuhl at the University of Pennsylvania, replaced the mechanical tapper bar of the dot scanner with a flashing light which produced a dot of light on photographic film. The intensity of the light varied with the counting rate, permitting visualization of smaller changes in the counting rate than was possible with the earlier dot scanner. In this manner lesions which differed little from normal tissue in their uptake of an isotope could be discerned.

A variation of the gamma ray scanners described above is the positron scanner. The annihilation of a positron by a negative electron results in the release, in opposite directions, of two gamma rays of exactly the same energy. In the positron scanner two scintillation counters are employed, placed on opposite sides of the patient's body so that each will detect one of the two gamma rays. When both detectors simultaneously record the reception of a gamma ray it means that a positron was liberated somewhere along the path of a straight line between the two detectors. Thus by visually recording only those events occurring when both detectors receive gamma rays simultaneously spurious information from scattered radiation is virtually eliminated.

A multi-detector positron scanner has been developed at Brookhaven National Laboratory for locating brain tumors. It employs a ring of detectors which fits over the patient's head. By utilizing many pairs of detection crystals, the scanning time is shortened.

The first whole-body scanner, developed in 1952 by Anger at Donner Laboratory, is still being used for diagnostic and research purposes. This scanner has ten scintillation counters, and is capable of scanning the whole body of a patient in 40 minutes with good sensitivity and resolution.

A high-energy gamma-ray scanner was designed and built at Sloan-Kettering Institute for Cancer Research in 1960. This instrument can detect tracer doses of radioisotopes which emit high-energy gamma rays. Its ability to do this is based on the use of tungsten rather than lead as a collimator. It has two heavily shielded, sensitive detectors, one mounted above and one below the bed on which the patient lies. These detectors can be programmed to move in various patterns over the entire body. The movements can be continuous or the detectors can be made to measure for a preset time at different positions before moving on.

An improvement recently made in the method of displaying imprint data obtained by scanning is the introduction of multi-color printout systems. The radioisotope distribution is still shown by the printing pattern, but in addition the variation in concentration is shown by the printing color. Mallard and Peachey described a color scanning system at the Hammersmith Hospital in England in 1959. In 1962 Kakehi reported a method for color scanning used at the Chiba University School of Medicine in Japan. Since March 1963 Hine, of the Boston Veterans Administration Hospital and the Boston University School of Medicine, has performed many color scans of various organs, including the thyroid, brain, kidney, and liver.

Development of Cameras

The scanning devices considered to this point all employ a time-consuming back and forth motion of the detector over the patient. There now appeared a group of scintillation cameras which were able to view the patient from a fixed position.

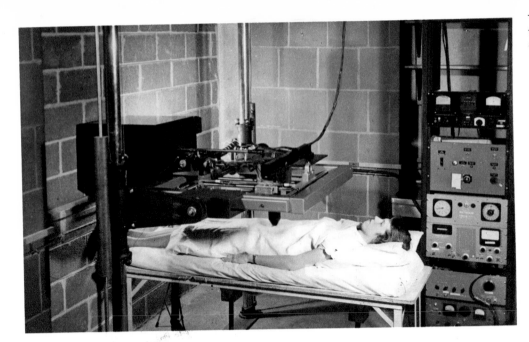

The first photoscanner. This machine was re-
tired late in 1963 after nearly ten years service
at the University of Pennsylvania.

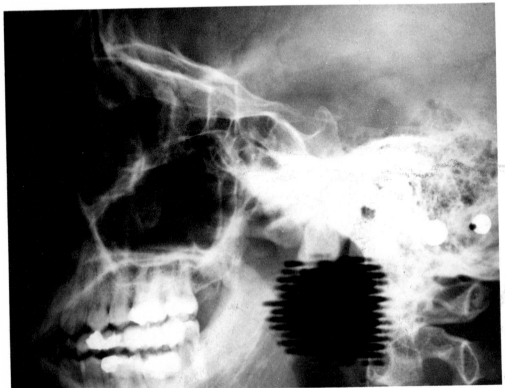

One of the first scans made by a photoscanner.
The photorecording, superimposed on an X-ray
picture for orientation, shows a metastasis in
the neck resulting from a thyroid carcinoma.

Opposite:
The multi-detector positron scanner developed
at Brookhaven National Laboratory for locating
brain tumors with positron-emitting isotopes. A
pair of gamma rays are detected simultaneously by an opposed pair of detection crystals,
and a line is established along which the tumor
is detected. By utilizing many pairs of detection
crystals, the scanning time is shortened and the
accuracy with which a tumor can be located is
increased.

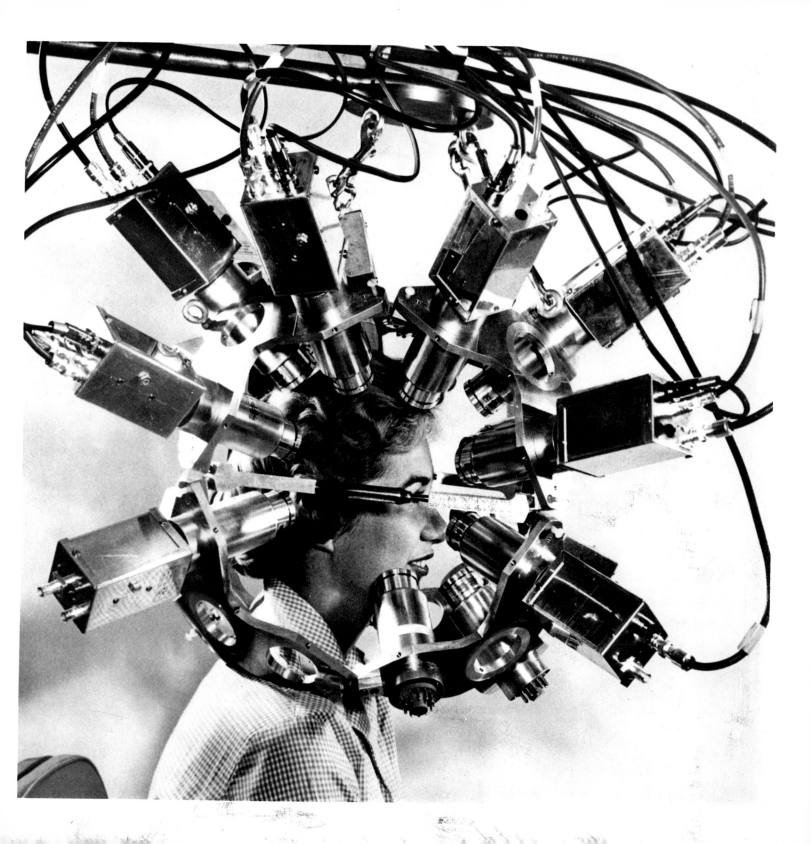

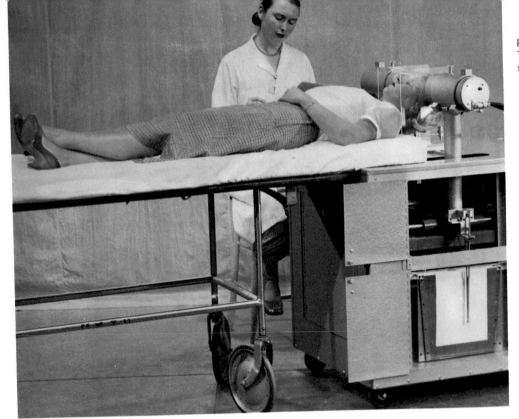

Positron scanner being used for brain scanning. Two detectors are employed, located on opposite sides of the patient's head.

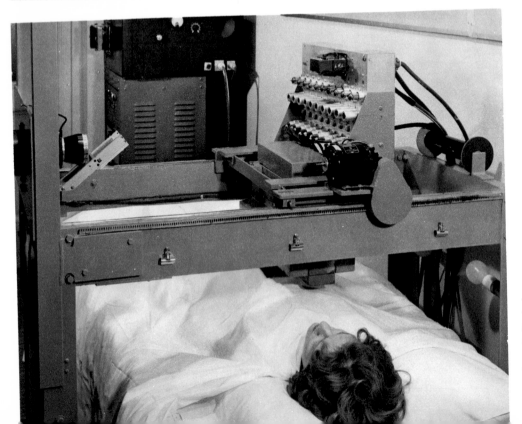

The first whole-body scanner, developed in 1952 and still being used. The lead collimator contains 10 scintillation counters and moves across the subject. The bed is moved by increments and serial scans are made and then joined together to form a head-to-toe picture of the subject.

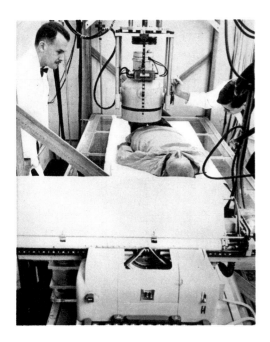

The high-energy gamma (HEG) scanner at Sloan-Kettering Institute records gamma-ray emissions as numbers on a large chart by means of an automated typewriter. The high digits indicate a heavy isotope uptake, plainly localizing the site of a bone lesion.

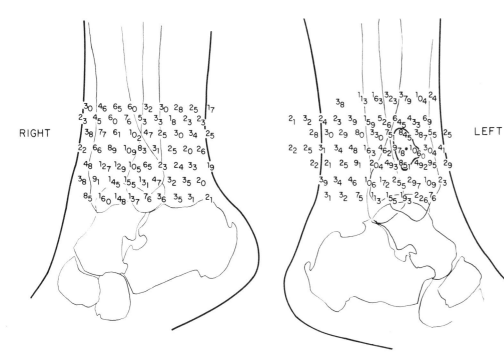

RIGHT   LEFT

Ankle scans made with the Sloan-Kettering scanner are superimposed on drawings made from X-ray pictures. The scans were done about two weeks after injecting 300 microcuries of strontium 85. The area of high uptake (large numbers), corresponding to osteoblastic lesions, is circled.

These new devices could therefore analyze isotope distribution rapidly, thus minimizing the time required for the patient to remain immobile. Furthermore, increased sensitivity permitted the use of lower isotope activities.

The speed of the new instruments also opened new dimensions in the study of organ function by their ability to keep pace with the relatively rapid movement of radioisotopes from one part of an organ to another. Such studies are important diagnostically because organ function can be disturbed long before there is any great structural change which would be sensed by X-ray pictures or other tests.

The first scintillation camera consisted of a pinhole collimator, a 4-inch diameter sodium iodide crystal, a bank of 7 photo-tubes, a computer circuit, a pulse height selector, and an oscilloscope. An improved version employs an 11½-inch sodium iodide crystal and a bank of 19 phototubes. The larger crystal permits the efficient use of multichannel collimators with 1,000 or more parallel holes. The collimator, which can be either a pin-hole or a multi-aperture type, defines the gamma ray image of the subject on the image detector crystal. This image is then translated electronically to a pattern on the oscillo-scope which when photographed by time exposure provides a scintiphoto. Exposure times of about 5 minutes are used when the normal scanning dose of tracer compound is administered. As with scans made by prior instruments, variations in lightness or darkness on the scintiphoto determine the presence of abnormalities. Time-lapse motion pictures have been made with the scintillation camera to record the passage of various substances through the liver, kidney and other organs.

A variation of the scintillation camera, the positron camera, can locate brain tumors with positron-emitting isotopes such as chelated gallium 68. This very complex device converts gamma-ray pairs into an image of the isotope distribution. The positron camera can make good pictures with diagnostic value in about 5 to 10 minutes, making possible the use of short-lived isotopes.

Another new experimental device based on the scintillation camera and developed at Roswell Park Memorial Institute, Buffalo, New York, is called the auto-

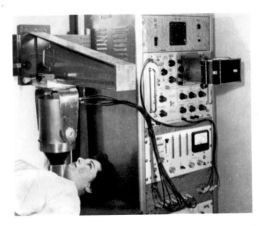

The gamma-ray scintillation camera has a pin-hole collimator. The lead-shielded scintillation crystal above the subject is monitored by a bank of photomultiplier tubes. A computing circuit transforms the location of scintillations to points of light on an oscilloscope, which is viewed by the Polaroid camera. The polaroid camera print delineates the distribution of gamma-emitting isotopes within areas such as the thyroid.

Positron scintillation camera being operated by H. O. Anger of Donner Laboratory who developed the device in 1958. Patient is positioned for taking brain scintiphotos. The camera setup at right of picture includes a computer circuit, pulse-height selector and an oscilloscope. The gamma ray pairs emitted by the tracer compound in the patient are converted to an image of the isotope distribution.

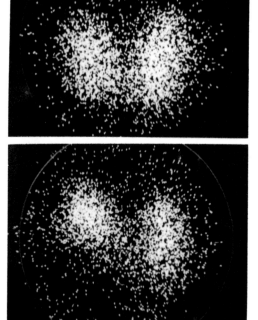

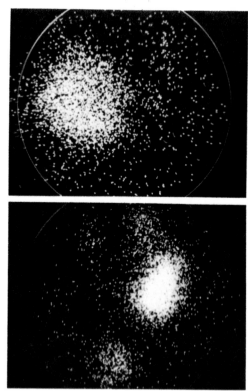

The autofluoroscope detector shown with its 2-inch lead shield removed. A bank of 293 sodium iodide crystals is in the lead-encased enclosure at bottom. This bank is separated from the 12 photomultiplier tubes by a 4-inch Lucite light pipe. The data are transferred electronically and recorded on Polaroid film.

Four neck scintiphotos of different individuals made with the gamma-ray scintillation camera 24 hours after administration of 25 to 50 microcuries of iodine 131.
Upper left: normal, butterfly-shaped, thyroid gland.
Upper right: Solitary toxic nodule in right lobe. This "hot" nodule takes up the iodine 131 to a greater extent than the normal thyroid tissue.
Lower left. Degenerating cyst seen as a dark area in lower left of picture. This "cold" nodule is non-functioning, hence does not take up the radioisotope.
Lower right: This patient had undergone a "total" thyroidectomy 2 years previously. The photo shows regrowth of functioning tissue, right, and also a metastasis, lower center.

Seven serial scans made with the whole body scanner were put together to provide a whole-body scan of this patient with thyroid cancer metastasized to the lung. One millicurie of iodine 131 was administered and the scan made 72 hours later. Note the uptake in the lung. This patient was successfully treated with large doses of iodine 131.

fluoroscope. This instrument has 293 sodium iodide crystals, each crystal having an individual collimated aperture.

Medical Studies with Scanners and Cameras

Scanning has proved a successful diagnostic technique primarily because radioisotopes or labeled compounds may concentrate to a different degree in various normal and neoplastic tissues. With proper selection of labeled substances the physician can therefore use scanners and cameras to study disturbed metabolism in a wide variety of disease conditions. Furthermore, by study of scans or scintiphotos of tumors, their treatment by surgery or radiotherapy can more easily be planned. Although the advantages of these techniques in diagnosis and medical research have yet to be fully exploited, some very promising uses have already been developed. Some of these are considered briefly below.

As has been indicated, the thyroid is among the easiest organs to scan because of its ability to concentrate iodine and its location near the skin surface. Thus it was possible to use the earliest dot scanners on the thyroid. A patient having a thyroid nodule may be given iodine 131. Scans or scintiphotos of a normal thyroid gland resemble a butterfly in outline. A "hot" nodule, which takes up more isotope than normal thyroid tissue, appears as a lighter area in the picture. This type of nodule is practically never cancerous. "Cold" nodules, which do not pick up the isotope, show as dark areas in the pictures. Most of these are subsequently examined by biopsy because 30 to 40% are found to be cancerous. The scintillation camera with triple-aperture pinhole collimator marked a step forward in diagnosing thyroid cancer, since three simultaneous views of the thyroid are taken, one from the front and two at oblique angles.

One of the early applications of the whole-body scanner was in the detection of iodine-131 uptake in metastatic lesions from thyroid cancer. These studies demonstrate the location of the lesions and also the relative uptake in the lesions.

The brain does not actively concentrate substances in the same manner as the thyroid concentrates iodine. Nevertheless,

it is possible to locate tumor tissue in the brain with certain labeled compounds, either because passive accumulation of substances may occur owing to increased permeability within the brain or tumor that results in a decreased ability of the blood-brain barrier to exclude a compound, or because of increased vascularity of the tumor tissue. Since 1954 various labeled compounds have been employed to locate brain tumors, but radioiodine in the form of iodinated human serum albumin (RISA) was the most frequently used substance until 1962. At that time, Blau and Bender at Roswell Park Memorial Institute began to use mercury-203-labeled neohydrin as an agent for this purpose. Mercury 203 has the advantages relative to radioiodine of emitting a single gamma ray of 0.28 MeV (an optimum energy for scanning), and also of providing a low background at the time of scanning because it is not concentrated in the overlying skin.

Several of the devices described earlier have been successful in locating brain tumors. The use of positron scanners and positron cameras for this purpose has already been referred to. The positron camera has in some cases been uniquely successful in detecting pituitary tumors. At Massachusetts General Hospital in Boston brain tumors are detected with a positron scanner and the positron-emitting isotope arsenic 74. The technique used there makes it possible to determine in which hemisphere of the brain a lesion is located since the shape of the marking varies according to which detector has the higher count rate. The gamma ray scintillation camera can visualize brain tumors with mercury-203-neohydrin in about 5 minutes. The positron camera can do so with gallium 68 in the same length of time, but only 1/1000 as much radiation need be delivered to the patient because of the short half-life of this isotope.

By means of the scintillation camera it is possible to show the size and location of the kidneys and liver and to study their function in one tenth the time required by conventional scanners. Time lapse motion pictures have been made with the scintillation camera to record the passage of substances through both the kidney and the liver. Pictured is an interesting example of how this procedure was used in

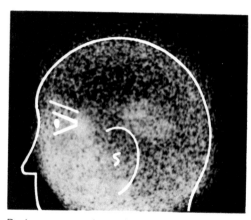

Brain scan made with positron scintillation camera and chelated gallium 68 demonstrates presence of tumor indicated by light area above ear. Light area in facial region is caused by uptake in bone and extracellular space.)

28

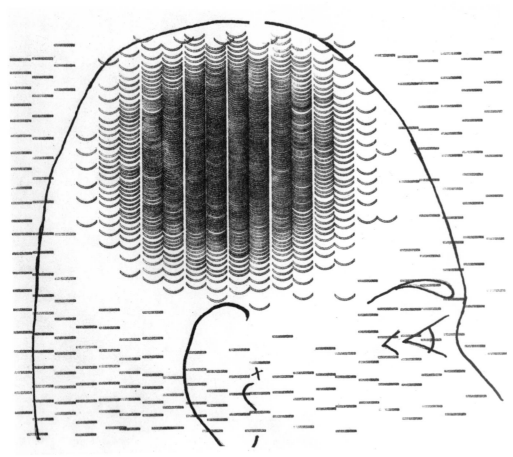

Brain scan made with positron scanner and arsenic 74. Curved markings indicate increased uptake to the right of the midline, and straight markings increased uptake to the left. In this case, the dense concentration of curved markings indicates a tumor on the surface of the right side of the brain; the sparce straight markings probably indicate that the patient was positioned slightly nearer to left detector.

Time-lapse motion pictures of the liver of a 3-year-old girl were made with the scintillation camera one hour after injection of 50 microcuries of iodine-131-labeled Rose Bengal. Exposure time was 2 minutes per frame. The bile duct system had failed to develop in this child and an artificial bile duct had been created surgically between the liver and duodenum. She developed symptoms which caused concern that the duct had closed. These scans show the bolus of activity (small light area) moving downward and to the right, indicating that the duct was still open.

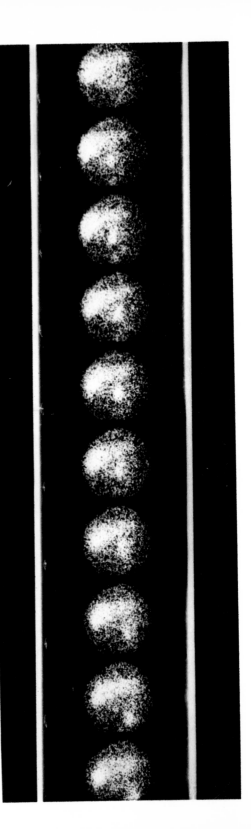

a liver study to demonstrate that an artificially created bile duct in a new-born infant was still functioning, thereby avoiding an unnecessary repeat operation.

Whole body scanners have been used to provide information necessary for performing needle biopsies to diagnose kidney or liver disease. By using a scan to guide the placement of the biopsy needle major exploratory surgery can be avoided when a lesion is suspected. Kidney scans have been successful in ascertaining the size and shape of the kidneys in persons with mild or moderate uremia, even when radiographic pyelograms showed nothing. In addition, scanning may be of particular value for those patients who are unable to have a pyelogram because of hypersensitivity to the dye required for the procedure.

Spleen scans are likely to come into general use because they are often more informative than examinations based on palpation or X-ray pictures. Those pictured were made with chromium 51-tagged red blood cells which had been altered by heat treatment. Such damaged cells are selectively removed by the spleen. Spleen scans will show position and size of the functioning spleen and indicate presence of splenic abscesses. They can help to determine whether or not a left upper quadrant abdominal mass is an enlarged spleen or to indicate an abnormal situation where the spleen is on the right side of the body. They also make it possible to detect an accessory spleen such as is sometimes found when persistent anemias occur after splenectomy.

To find a suitable labeled compound with which to scan the pancreas, investigators at Roswell Park Memorial Institute utilized the fact that the pancreas synthesizes digestive enzymes rapidly— five to ten per cent of amino acids administered intravenously are found in the pancreas within one hour. They developed a substance, selenium-75-seleno-methionine, which has all the properties of the amino acid methionine and is taken up by the pancreas. This technique has had some success in detecting both benign and malignant tumors of the pancreas. It is also possible to use it to diagnose acute pancreatitis based on the fact that persons with

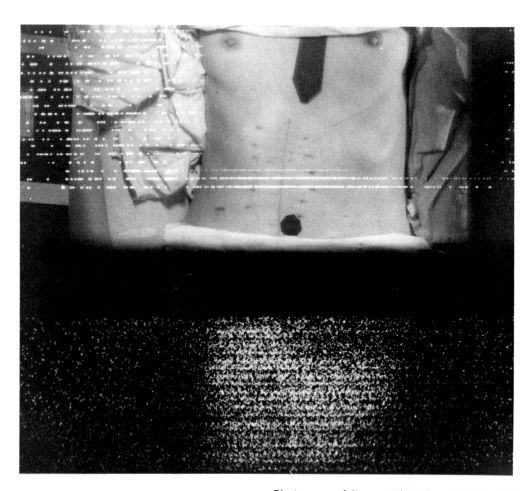

Photoscan of liver, with iodine-131-labeled Rose Bengal showing liver enlarged in all dimensions with a distinct area of very low concentration of the isotope in the middle of the right lobe due to amoebic abscess.

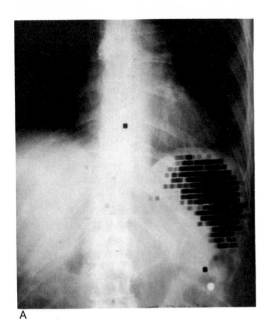

A

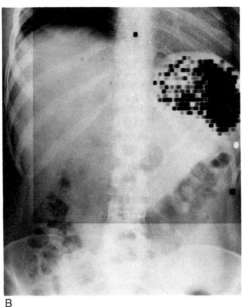

B

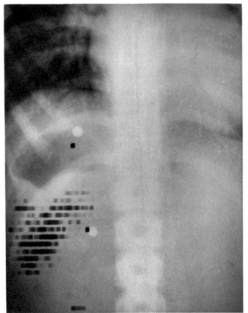

C

Spleen scans made with chromium-51-tagged red blood cells which had been altered by heat treatment. Such damaged cells are selectively removed by the speen.
A) Normal speen.
B) Intrasplenic abcess. Note ring of radioactivity surrounding the area of decreased activity at medial portion of the spleen.
C) Scan shows that patient's spleen is on the right side of the abdomen—normally it is on the left side as in the other scans.

that disease show no uptake of the isotope.

Medical scientists have of course been interested in improving techniques that will aid in the diagnosis and treatment of heart disease, the leading cause of mortality in the United States. Scanning with RISA has proved useful in differentiating between enlargement of the heart and fluid around the heart. The information that fluid is present can be of importance in the management of patients with pericarditis. Radiocardiography with technetium 99m has also proven useful in diagnosing heart disease. This short-lived isotope (half-life 6 hr.) can be produced readily in the laboratory from the parent isotope molybdenum 99 (half-life 67 hr.). (See later discussion on short-lived isotopes.)

Several scanning techniques have proven useful in the detection of bone abnormalities. The whole body scanner with fluorine 18 has been used to detect bone lesions in patients with metastatic breast cancer. The positron camera and positron-emitting iron 52 have provided clear pictures of the marrow compartments of large bones. Investigators at the Sloan-Kettering Institute, employing the high-energy gamma scanner described earlier, have been able to study the distribution and turnover rates of the bone seeking isotopes calcium 47 and strontium 85 with very small amounts of these isotopes. Calcium 47 studies have been helpful in evaluating the relative effects on calcium kinetics of various types of treatment such as radiation therapy, hormone therapy, and hypophysectomy (removal of the pituitary gland). Calcium 47, strontium 85, and strontium 87m have been used for the early detection of bone metastases not visible in X-ray pictures.

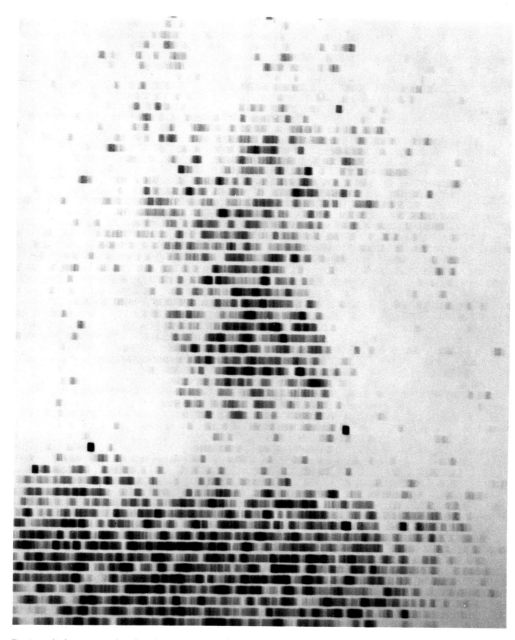

Pericardial scan made after intravenous administration of 100 microcuries of RISA (iodine-131-labeled human serum albumin). Note the bank of decreased activity separating the cardiac (center) and liver (below) blood pools. This is because of fluid around the heart. Normally the two pools appear to be fused.

Whole Body Counters

The need to measure the radioactivity in the body acquired accidentally, such as from radioactive fallout or from accidents in nuclear installations, stimulated the development of instruments which could quickly count the radioactivity in entire human bodies. Since the Geneva Conference in 1958, when the pioneering work with the original United States whole body counters was described, the number of these very sensitive units has markedly increased. As of early 1964 there were more than 130 in operation, some 44 of which were in the United States. In radiological health work they have proven of great value, and in medical diagnosis and research their great potential is just beginning to be realized. Their great sensitivity makes it possible to detect even natural levels of radioactivity within the body. Also, when isotopes are administered for diagnostic purposes it is possible by using whole body counters to keep the dosage low and to study absorption and elimination rates for various substances without the inconvenience of collecting and analyzing excretions.

Types of Counters

All whole body counters must have a very sensitive detector which reacts to gamma rays, a device to exhibit and/or record the number of these reactions, and adequate shielding to reduce radiation from sources other than the body being counted. The shield is usually a room, large enough to comfortably hold a person, with walls of asbestos, chalk, concrete, or lead, or of steel low in radioisotope content.

The most widely used type of whole body counter, developed by Miller and Marinelli at Argonne National Laboratory in 1955, employs a large sodium iodide crystal. The person being counted usually sits in a tilted chair in such a way that he essentially surrounds the detector, all parts of his body except the lower limbs being approximately 16 inches away from it. Some counters have both the chair and the "one-meter arc couch" When possible the arc position is preferred because the counting rate is less dependent upon variations of location of the isotope within the body. However, when greater sensitivity is required the chair is employed.

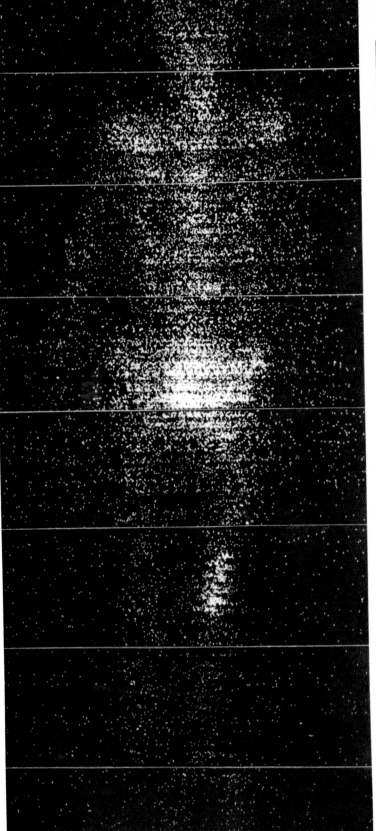

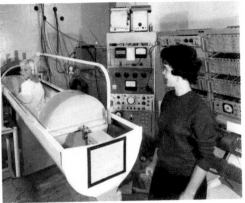

The liquid scintillation whole body counter developed by Anderson and co-workers at Los Alamos Scientific Laboratory in 1953. In this system the subject's body is surrounded by a double walled tank filled with a gamma-detecting liquid. This large detector provides great sensitivity because it can intercept a large fraction of the gamma rays emitted from the body. The resolving power, however, is less than that of the crystal counter.

Whole-body scan of patient, with bone metastases from breast carcinoma, made with fluorine 18. Note the concentration of the isotope in the sites of the bone lesions: right shoulder; portions of pelvis, (especially on left); and distal left femur. (The very bright spot in the center of the pelvis represents bladder concentration.)

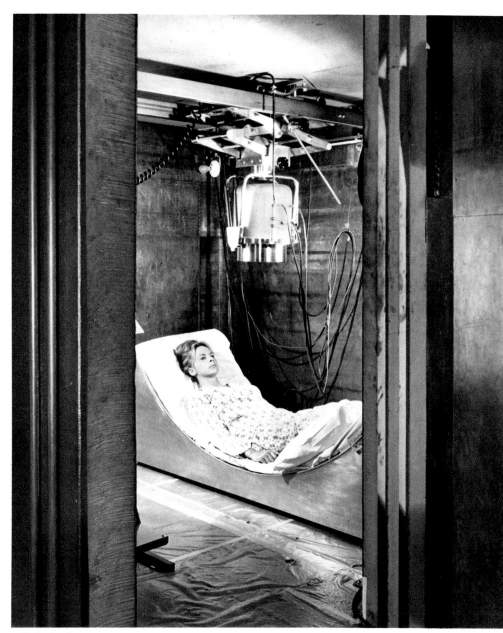

Whole body counter: one wall of the massive steel shield can be seen at the far left. The patient is lying in the "one meter arc couch" with sodium iodide crystal above. The arc position is preferred when possible because the counting rate is less dependent upon variation of location of the isotope within the body.

Another type of counter, originally developed by Anderson and co-workers at Los Alamos Scientific Laboratory in 1953, employs a liquid scintillator. Instead of the subject's body surrounding the detector, the detector surrounds the subject. He is placed on a bed that is either half or wholly surrounded by a double walled tank filled with a gamma-detecting liquid. In a variant of this type the liquid is replaced by blocks of plastic sensitive to gamma rays.

The principle advantage of the crystal type of detector is that it permits sharp resolution of photopeaks so that individual isotopes can be identified by utilizing pulse-height analyzers, even when the isotopes have only slightly different energies. This is an important advantage in diagnoses where two or more isotopes may be used simultaneously to provide different information, and also in the measurement and identification of radioactivity in the body when unknown radioisotopes may be present.

Because of their geometrical arrangement, liquid and plastic scintillators intercept a much larger fraction of the gamma rays leaving the body. This increased efficiency permits measurements to be made in a much shorter time than with the crystal system. On the other hand, as noted above, the liquid and plastic scintillators have relatively poor resolving power—they are not capable of distinguishing two radioisotopes unless their respective energies differ widely.

Practically all the whole body counters in the United States have crystal detectors, the distribution as of early 1964 being 40 crystal, 3 liquid and 1 plastic.

Medical Studies with Whole Body Counters

At Brookhaven National Laboratory the ability of individuals to absorb vitamin B_{12} has been studied with whole body counters. Lack of this ability can be symptomatic of either pernicious anemia or intestinal malabsorption.

The standard method for measuring vitamin B_{12} absorption has been the so-called Schilling test. This involves giving an oral dose of the vitamin labeled with radioactive cobalt, injecting a massive flushing dose of non-radioactive vitamin B_{12}, and then collecting urine for 24 hours and assaying it for radiocobalt.

The study at Brookhaven utilizing the

whole body counting technique measured simultaneously the retention of free vitamin B_{12} labeled with cobalt 58, and intrinsic-factor-bound vitamin B_{12} labeled with cobalt 60, following oral administration of these substances. The results, as in the Schilling test, clearly distinguished among three groups of subjects; those with pernicious anemia, those with intestinal malabsorption, and those who were normal.

The chief advantage of using the whole body counter for this determination is that it measures vitamin B_{12} absorption directly, thus distinguishing intrinsic factor deficiency from intestinal malabsorption as a cause of the disorder much more simply than does the Schilling test. In addition it does not require the use of non-physiological massive therapeutic doses, and it avoids the difficulties and possibilities of error involved in the collecting and analyzing of urine samples.

Whole body counter studies of the absorption of vitamin B_{12} have also been conducted at Vanderbilt University, the vitamin being labeled with cobalt 57. Findings there indicated that vitamin B_{12} losses are similar in normal persons, in patients with pernicious anemia who are receiving large replacement doses of the vitamin, and in patients with pernicious anemia who are receiving minimal replacement of the vitamin. This would indicate a mechanism for loss of B_{12} from the body which is relatively independent of the body content. The so-called biological half life of cobalt-labeled vitamin B_{12} in the body is of the order of one year.

Iron plays a vital role in human health, the lack of it leading to lowered vitality and to illness. It is probable that more people suffer from iron deficiency than from any other deficiency. It is known that the percentage absorption of iron in the diet is normally not high, and also that iron is retained in the body and is excreted very slowly. However, all the facts about iron absorption and excretion in health and disease are not yet known and the whole body counter is proving to be of great value in assistance toward gaining the missing information.

In one study of a group of normal subjects, radioactive iron 59 was given orally and its absorption measured. This provided a standard with which to compare deviations observed in a variety of diseases. It was found that the percent of absorption was directly proportional to the percent of reticulocytes present in the peripheral blood. The reticulocytes are an index of the production of red blood cells, so that this correlation reflects one control mechanism of the body which adjusts the amount of iron absorbed to the amount needed for manufacture of new red cells. The iron retained in the body was also determined over a period of 10 months. These findings disclosed that even healthy persons lose iron equivalent to approximately one milliliter of blood daily. Further study of stool collections showed that the most probable route was in blood lost normally through the intestinal wall. This finding underscores the importance of understanding and eliminating many of the gastrointestinal diseases prevalent throughout the world, because it is probable that a major cause of iron deficiency in man is iron loss from infection and hemorrhage (often microscopic) in the gastrointestinal tract.

Iron 59 has also been used with whole body counters to study blood loss from various types of hemorrhage, including acute and chronic gastrointestinal bleeding. Such measurements can often be used to quantitate blood loss from the body before it can be detected by any other means. This information is of value clinically in the early detection of cancer and other diseases of the gastrointestinal tract. Excessive menstrual blood loss has been similarly studied.

Other studies involving iron loss have been conducted with the Vanderbilt University whole body counter. These concerned a rare disorder, paroxysmal nocturnal hemoglobinuria, in which red blood cells break up and the hemoglobin appears in the urine. With iron 59 it was demonstrated that the rate of iron loss in these patients was three to eight times normal.

Another significant contribution of the whole body counter has been in the study of calcium metabolism, so important in understanding and diagnosing many diseases involving bone. Studies at Donner Laboratory with calcium 47, a short-lived, gamma-emitting isotope, have shown readily measurable differences in calcium metabolism between normal persons, on the one hand, and patients with

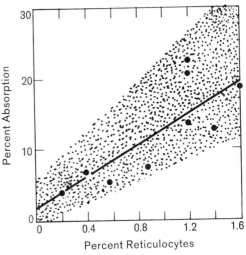

Correlation of percent of iron absorbed and the percent of reticulocytes. Because the reticulocytes are an index of the production of red blood cells, this correlation reflects one control mechanism of the body by which the amount of iron absorbed is adjusted to the amount needed for manufacture of new red cells.

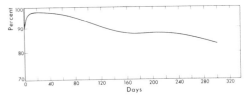

Whole body iron-59 retention of 10 normal subjects followed for 300 days. The indicated loss of iron from the body is considered to represent chiefly a small regular loss of blood from the intestines of normal people.

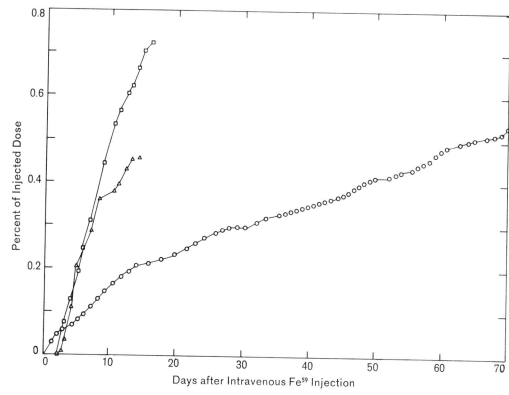

Cumulative radioiron excreted in stools of three subjects expressed as percent of injected dose. Slope after 10 days is considered to represent small continuous loss of blood through the intestinal wall (slope during first 10 days includes sloughing of iron in mucosal epithelium).

acromegaly, cancer with metastatic bone lesions, and hypercalcemia of diverse etiology on the other. Such studies may therefore provide a tool for diagnosing these conditions and may also furnish fundamental information concerning the disease processes. In acromegalic patients, for example, the amount of calcium retention permits the physician to assess the activity of the disease.

The body possesses a built-in tracer, potassium 40, which is a naturally occurring gamma-ray and beta-ray emitter with a half-life of more than a billion years. The quantity of potassium 40 in the body is so minute, however, that it was not until the advent of the whole body counter that one could detect this isotope and thereby employ it in tracer studies. Potassium is distributed nearly everywhere in the body except in the fatty tissue. From this fact has come a new technique which utilizes potassium 40 to determine the body's lean tissue mass. This measurement can be important in assessing such factors as the body composition of populations; the changes that take place normally throughout the life-span and during disease; the relationships to nutrition; and the correlations with other physiological measurements such as metabolic rate and blood volume.

The validity of the whole body potassium-40 method for assessing lean body mass has been tested by comparison with other methods. One of the most prominent of these has been a method based on the determination of total body water using tritium as a tracer. This provides a good measure of lean body mass, but it is not infallible. Siri and his co-workers have used the combination of total body water, body volume, and density, the latter measured by the helium displacement technique, to obtain a somewhat more precise determination. Whole body potassium 40 counts have shown a high correlation with determinations of lean body mass made by these other methods (although there is some uncertainty introduced by the body shape and size when counters are employed) and have the advantages of convenience and of not requiring the administration of a radioisotope.

The measurement of naturally occurring potassium 40 can be of importance in

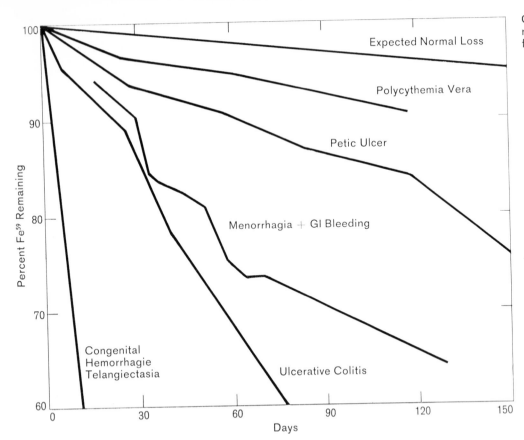

Comparison of iron loss from the body in the normal subject and in patients with several different diseases.

Expected Normal Loss

Polycythemia Vera

Petic Ulcer

Menorrhagia + GI Bleeding

Congenital Hemorrhagie Telangiectasia

Ulcerative Colitis

(Y-axis: Percent Fe⁵⁹ Remaining; X-axis: Days)

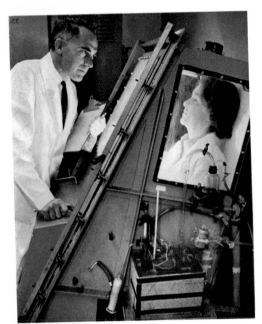

William Siri with the chamber used for determining body volume. This is computed by measuring the total displacement of helium. By using the body volume and total body water determinations (from tritiated water) together, one can derive the amount of total body fat and lean body mass.

Amounts of fat and lean tissue in normal subjects. The determinations were based on data from percent body water determined with tritiated water and from body volume and specific gravity determined in the helium chamber.
A) Distributions of percent fat in body for men and women.
B) Average relative amounts of fat and lean tissue for men and women, and for lean and obese people.

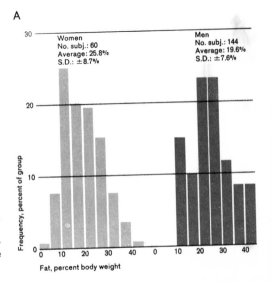

A

Women
No. subj.: 60
Average: 25.8%
S.D.: ±8.7%

Men
No. subj.: 144
Average: 19.6%
S.D.: ±7.6%

(Y-axis: Frequency, percent of group; X-axis: Fat, percent body weight)

investigative studies, and may also have diagnostic value in some diseases of muscle, particularly muscular dystrophy. It has long been known that potassium plays an important role in the energy release during muscular contraction. However, attempts to measure changes in serum potassium levels have been unsuccessful because 95% of the potassium in the body is intracellular, so that changes in this concentration are usually not reflected in the serum levels. Attempts to use artificially produced potassium 42 (half-life 12.5 hr) have been similarly unsuccessful because the change of the labeled potassium with the intracellular fluid is too slow a process to be completed in the short time during which this short-lived isotope can be detected.

Whole body potassium 40 measurements are of particular value in the study of muscular dystrophy because the children or other apparently healthy relatives of patients may also be studied without administering a radioactive tracer. Such studies at the University of California at Los Angeles suggest that there may be a gradual and progessive wasting of body potassium during the onset and course of muscular dystrophy. At the present time it is not known if such changes occur prior to, or as a result of, the disease. However, when close relatives of muscular dystrophy patients were studied, lowered total potassium values were found in a number of instances. This evidence suggests the presence of a lowered potassium content prior to recognition of the disease, perhaps as a result of an inherited intracellular defect. Thus, the whole body counter may assume a role in diagnosing muscular dystrophy in its preclinical stages, and in unraveling the mysteries of the disease.

It is especially important in isotope studies on infants and small children to keep the radiation exposure low. The administered dose can be greatly reduced if the studies are carried out within the whole body counter room. This is well illustrated by thyroid studies. In the early days when only Geiger Counters were employed such studies commonly required 50 to 100 microcuries of radioiodine. With the development of the scintillation counter the doses were cut to a few microcuries. Whole body counters can readily detect ac-

The total body water is determined by the dilution method, using tritiated water. This shows a technician purifying the urine sample so that the tritium content can be determined and the body water calculated.

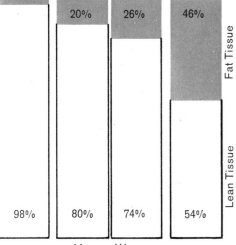

B
Lean 98% / Men Average 80% 20% / Women 74% 26% / Obese 54% 46%
Fat Tissue / Lean Tissue

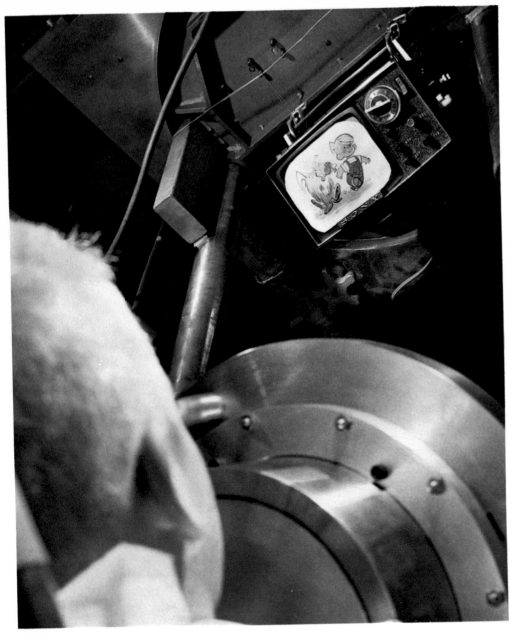

A technique for measuring radioiodine uptake in the thyroid gland with nanocurie amounts of mixture of iodine 131 and iodine 125 requires that the counting be done in the whole body counting facility.
A: a small television set, mounted above the crystal in such a way that good viewing requires that the head be kept in the desired position, helps solve the problem of keeping small children still during a 15-minute counting period.
B: a child in position for a thyroid uptake study.

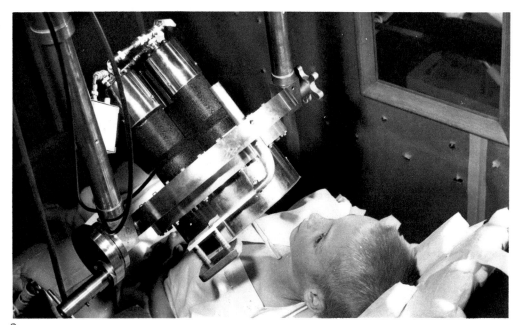

B

tivities of iodine 131 as small as 0.1 microcurie or less and the exposure can be cut still further by using iodine 125, which does not emit beta rays (iodine 131 emits both beta and gamma rays).

Whole body counters are being used at Argonne National Laboratory, Argonne Cancer Research Hospital, and other centers in continuing studies of the late effects of metabolism of bone seeking radio-elements. One of the elements being studied is radium. Two groups of people are serving as subjects. One consists of patients who, many years ago, before the dangers of indiscriminate exposure to radium were understood, received therapeutic doses which would now be considered dangerous. The other consists of some 1,000 persons who thirty to forty years ago, while employed to paint watch dials with radium-containing paint, were in the habit of "pointing" their brushes with their lips and tongue, resulting in the ingestion of small quantities of radium.

A systematic study of all such exposed individuals is now providing information on the relationship between the retained "body burden" and the long term effects of internally deposited alpha-emitting isotopes, as well as on procedures which may be of value in removing them from bone and other tissues. The data from whole body counting are being gathered concerning total body content, rate of elimination of radium, time elapsed since acquisition, degree of skeletal radiation damage, incidence of neoplasia, and the earliest possible time when significant orthopedic damage or neoplasms can be detected. The results are directed toward the development of quantitative data necessary to the establishment of accurate "permissible levels" of bone-seeking isotopes such as radium and plutonium.

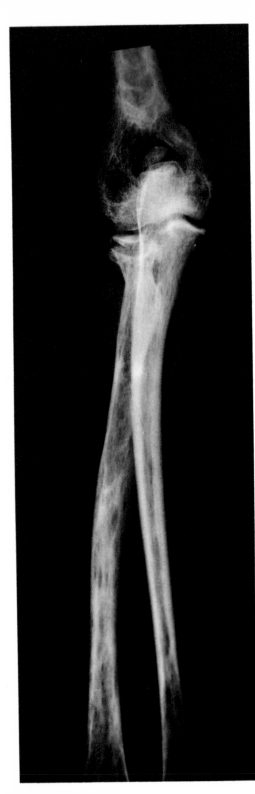

Typical destructive changes in bone in a former radium dial painter.

Table I
Half-Lives of Radioisotopes Classified for Applications In Medical Diagnosis

Very Short-Lived	Less than 1 Minute
Short-Lived	1 Minute to 1 Hour
Medium-Lived	1 Hour to 1 Day
Long-Lived	1 Day to 1 Week
Very Long-Lived	More than 1 Week

Short-Lived Isotopes

Short-lived isotopes can be arbitrarily defined as those with half-lives of less than a day (Another classification sometimes used is shown in Table I.) They have important advantages for use in medical research and diagnosis. Their rapid decay reduces to a minimum the radiation dosage given the subject. As pointed out above, this is especially important when children are involved. Further, since the residual activity with a short-lived isotope soon becomes negligible, it is possible to repeat studies at short intervals on the same subject.

The rapid loss of radioactivity which makes the use of short-lived isotopes advantageous also creates a major problem: how can the isotopes be made available at the time and place needed? One solution is to produce them in a reactor or accelerator at or near the place of intended use. The installation of a substantial number of small reactors and accelerators at sites close to medical schools, hospitals, and biological research laboratories in the United States is testimony to the frequent adoption of this solution. Reactors are the more convenient and economical source in most cases. However, there are many short-lived isotopes, especially positron emitters, which can be made only or more easily by a cyclotron or an accelerator (Tables II and III).

The first application of a short-lived positron emitter occurred in an aviation-medical study in 1944 on the problem of carbon monoxide poisoning. The isotope was carbon 11, which has a half-life of 20 minutes. The carbon monoxide labeled with this isotope was made in the 60-inch cyclotron at the University of California, Berkeley, it being only a 2 minute dash from there to the Donner Laboratory where the experiment was performed. The subjects breathed the carbon monoxide mixed with oxygen, and the expired air was collected in special bags and analyzed immediately. A Geiger counter also "looked at" a canister containing a carbon dioxide absorber, thus measuring any radioactive carbon monoxide converted to carbon dioxide. These studies showed that there was no significant conversion of carbon monoxide to carbon dioxide in the human body. Other studies on inert gas

Table II

Some medically useful short-lived
gamma-emitting isotopes

Element	Isotope	Half-life
Sodium	Na^{24}	15.0 hrs.
Magnesium	Mg^{28}	21.0 hrs.
Silicon	Si^{31}	2.6 hrs.
Potassium	K^{42}	12.5 hrs.
Calcium	Ca^{47}	113.0 hrs.
Manganese	Mn^{56}	2.6 hrs.
Nickel	Ni^{65}	2.6 hrs.
Zinc	Zn^{69m}	13.8 hrs.
Gallium	Ga^{72}	14.0 hrs.
Arsenic	As^{76}	26.0 hrs.
Bromine	Br^{82}	36.0 hrs.
Strontium	Sr^{87m}	2.8 hrs.
Molybdenum	Mo^{99}	67.0 hrs.
Technetium	Tc^{99m}	6.0 hrs.
Iodine	I^{123}	13.0 hrs.
Iodine	I^{130}	12.5 hrs.
Barium	Ba^{137m}	2.6 min.
Lanthanum	La^{140}	40.0 hrs.
Paraseodymium	Pr^{142}	19.2 hrs.
Dysprosium	Dy^{165}	2.3 hrs.
Tungsten	W^{187}	24.0 hrs.
Mercury	Hg^{197}	65.0 hrs.

Table III

Some medically useful positron-emitting
isotopes produced by cyclotrons

Element	Isotope	Half-life
*Carbon	C^{11}	20 min.
Nitrogen	N^{13}	10 min.
Oxygen	O^{15}	2 min.
*Fluorine	F^{18}	1.9 hr.
Sodium	Na^{22}	2.6 yr.
Chromium	Cr^{49}	42 min.
Iron	Fe^{52}	8.3 hr.
Cobalt	Co^{55}	18.2 hr.
*Copper	Cu^{64}	12.8 hr.
Gallium	Ga^{68}	1.1 hr.
Arsenic	As^{72}	1.1 days
Arsenic	As^{74}	17.5 days
Technetium	Tc^{94}	54 min.
Iodine	I^{124}	4.5 days

*Can also be produced in a reactor.

exchange, using radioactive nitrogen, krypton, argon, and xenon, were carried out at that time also, with particular reference to the problem of aviator's bends.

One of the several medical centers which has its own low power reactor for production of short-lived isotopes is the United States Naval Hospital in Bethesda, Maryland. Investigators there use iodine 128 (half-life 25 minutes) for 30 minute iodine uptake studies. This is of value in screening out patients with normal thyroid function to eliminate them from further studies with the longer-lived iodine 131. Iodine 128 represents a further example of the advantage cited earlier for short-lived isotopes: that they permit repeated studies on the same patient at relatively short intervals. If a test with iodine 128 is made in the morning, the same test can be repeated or another test using a different isotope performed in the afternoon of the same day.

Certain short-lived isotopes can also be made available by an alternative system whereby the desired isotope is "milked" from a longer-lived parent. The parent-daughter equilibrium mixture is shipped to the place of use and the short-lived daughter isotope separated there as needed. This technique has sharply accelerated the use of radioisotopes in medicine, 15 to 20 such mother-daughter combinations being in use today. One of the newest and most promising of these involves obtaining technetium 99m (half-life 6 hr) from molybdenum 99 (half-life 67 hr).

We have already referred to the successful use of positron-emitting gallium 68 (half-life 68 minutes) in brain tumor studies. The use of this and other short-lived positron emitting isotopes is made possible by the so-called "positron cow". When gallium 68 is involved, the "cow" consists of an ion exchange column containing a gallium-68—germanium-68 equilibrium mixture. The gallium 68 can be separated in the laboratory from the parent isotope, germanium 68, and used at once.

Myers, at Ohio State University, has used the isotope strontium 87m (half-life 2.8 hr), which emits gamma rays during its transition to the stable isotope strontium 87, for bone scans. This short-lived isotope can be "milked" readily from the cyclotron-produced, long-lived parent, yttrium 87 (half-life 80 hr). It can often replace strontium 85 (half-life 65 days) in bone

studies because the turnover rates are very rapid in certain bone diseases.

At the Washington University Medical Center in St. Louis, Missouri, the new cyclotron, installed early in 1964, has been set up so that the isotopes of several gases can be piped directly to hospital laboratories. One of the isotopes which will be "tamed" in this manner is oxygen 15, whose half-life is only 2.25 minutes. This will make possible more extensive research on oxygen kinetics and metabolism. One of the first projects employing oxygen 15 will be a study of oxygen exchange across the alveoli of the lung in emphysema. The patients will inhale oxygen containing oxygen 15. Then, with the aid of a counter, the rate of oxygen absorption by the blood will be determined. Although X-ray pictures may often determine the presence of emphysema, the oxygen 15 studies will be of additional help in determining functional changes associated with the disease. The use of oxygen 15 should also make easier the diagnosis of certain heart ailments by making possible comparisons of oxygen levels in limbs and lungs without recourse to arterial catheterization as presently required. This isotope may also make possible a technique whereby metabolic rates may be determined almost instantaneously.

As noted above another gas which can be piped and used directly is carbon monoxide labeled with positron-emitting carbon 11 (half-life 20.5 minutes). This gas attaches itself to hemoglobin and thus provides a simple and rapid method for labeling red blood cells. Where facilities are available for handling carbon 11, this method seems likely to replace in some situations the use of chromium 51 (half-life 27.8 days) as a means of determining red cell volume since the radiation within the body diminishes more rapidly with the shorter-lived isotope and the cells do not have to be removed from the body for the labeling process. Other gases, such as the short-lived isotopes of nitrogen, and the inert gases argon and krypton, will also be found useful.

Pioneering work similar to that at Washington University has been carried out with the cyclotron in the Hammersmith Hospital and Post Graduate Medical School in London, especially in pulmonary and cardiac function studies.

42

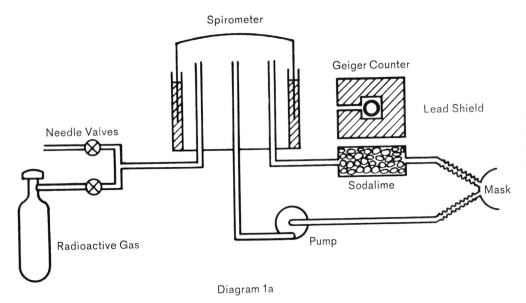

Spirometer

Geiger Counter

Lead Shield

Needle Valves

Sodalime

Mask

Radioactive Gas

Pump

Diagram 1a

This is the so-called "positron cow," the set-up whereby a short-lived isotope is "milked" from its longer-lived parent isotope. In this example gallium 68 (half-life 68 minutes) is being obtained from germanium 68 (half-life 275 days). The EDTA solution (ethylenediamine tetraacetic acid) is poured into the top of a column containing Alumina (aluminum trioxide) — germanium 68. After it passes through a sintered glass filter it is collected in a beaker as gallium-68-labeled EDTA solution. The germanium 68 remains in the column where a new supply of gallium 68 builds up in 1 to 2 hours. Gallium 68, a short-lived positron emitter, is useful for detecting brain tumors with the positron camera.

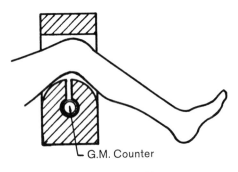

G.M. Counter

Lead Shield for
Measurement of Activity
in the Knee Region

Diagram 1b

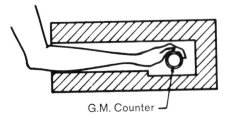

G.M. Counter

Lead Shield for
Measurement of Activity
in the Hand Region

Diagram 1c

Early apparatus used for radioactive gas exchange measurements in 1944. Diagram 1a shows the spirometer, mask, gas re-circulating system, and the Geiger Counter to detect radioactive carbon dioxide absorbed by the soda lime. Diagrams 1b and 1c show set-ups for measurement of radioactivity in the knee and hand regions, respectively.

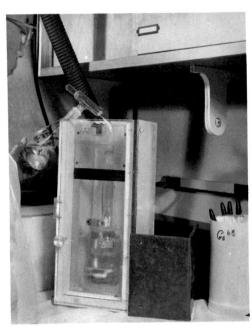

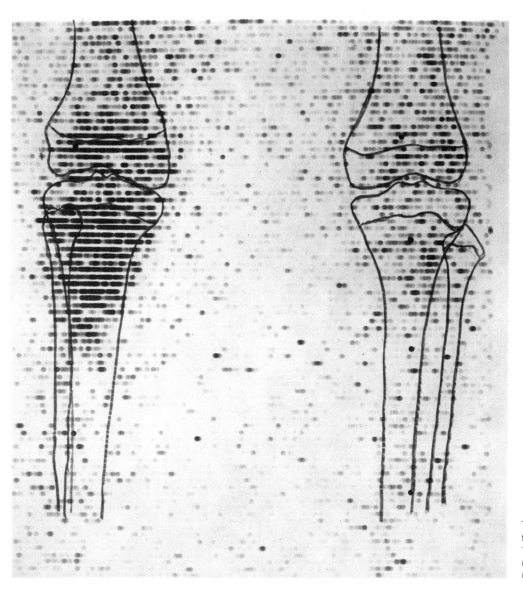

This is a bone scan made with short-lived strontium 87m (half-life 2.8 hours). The patient was a 13-year-old girl with a bone sarcoma of the right tibia. The greater strontium uptake in the right leg indicates the presence of the lesion.

The new 33-inch cyclotron at the Washington University School of Medicine, St. Louis, Missouri. This picture, taken in February 1964 while it was being installed, shows the magnets in the center of the picture.

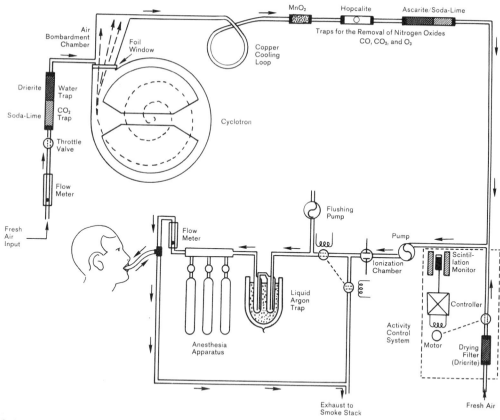

Schematic diagram showing the set-up for the generation, purification, and activity control of oxygen 15 (half-life 2.25 min.). This radioactive gas, as well as others, is piped directly from the cyclotron to the hospital laboratory for immediate use, thereby making possible studies with short-lived isotopes.

Trace Elements

Three methods based on radiation have been developed for the detection and measurement of trace elements—those occurring in such small concentrations that classical analytical techniques cannot measure them, often cannot even detect them. Despite the small quantities involved, some of these elements play a very important role in the normal functioning of the human body.

The three methods, neutron activation analysis, optical emission spectroscopy, and X-ray fluorescence spectroscopy, are based on the fact that if trace elements are either "excited" or rendered radioactive by an external energy source they will in the course of returning to their stable-state give off emissions with specific energies, or undergo characteristic decay patterns with specific energies and half-lives, by means of which the trace elements themselves can be identified and measured.

In activation analysis radioactivity is induced in a sample of material by exposing it to a high-energy radiation source, such as neutrons from reactors or other generators, particles from accelerators, or even gamma rays. The subsequent analysis of the radioactivity decay pattern permits identification and quantitation of the elements of interest. In optical emission spectroscopy the excitation energy comes from an arc lamp. This heat source affects the electrons in the outer shells of the atom. The "excited" element then emits optical energies with specific wave lengths which can be analyzed. X-ray fluorescence spectroscopy employs X rays for excitation energy. This higher energy source knocks electrons out of the inner shells of the atom, and the "excited" element then emits X rays with wave lengths characteristic for each element, which, again, can be analyzed.

While these methods offer great promise, it will be seen in the following discussion that the work with each is still in a very early stage.

Activation Analysis

The first application of neutron activation analysis for detection of trace elements is biological tissues occurred in 1947 when

This shows the set-up for X-ray emission spectroscopy. The large unit at the lower left is the X-ray generator; the small unit sitting on top is the spectrometer (see below); the tall unit to the right houses the pulse-height analysis and counting equipment.

This is a close-up view of the spectrometer. The sample is placed in the sample chamber located in the center between the X-ray tube (upper left) and crystal chamber (center right). The sample is then irradiated and the emitted X-rays are guided by the collimator to the detector (farthest to the right). The signal is then transferred to the pulse-height analyzer and the counting done. The counting data (after appropriate corrections for background and calibration) yield the elemental composition of the sample analyzed.

research teams at the University of California and at Argonne National Laboratory in Chicago independently employed the reactors at Hanford and Argonne, respectively, for activating samples of tissue and blood. Their results demonstrated that this method could detect elements such as iodine and gold in parts per 1,000,000,000 or less, and today many trace elements are being studied utilizing this technique.

Variations in the amount of iodine in the blood stream may reflect thyroid gland function and deviations from the normal may indicate thyroid disease. The normal concentration of iodine which is associated with thyroid hormones in human serum is quite low—$0.05 \mu g/ml$. Neutron activation analysis can detect less than $0.001 \mu g$. (one-billionth of a gram). At the present time, however, it is not feasible to adopt this method as a routine laboratory procedure because of the elaborate fractionation procedure required for the removal of chlorides and bromides. This problem will undoubtedly be solved in the near future.

The inhalation of manganese ore dust has been linked to a syndrome similar to spontaneous Parkinson's disease. In order to investigate this relationship, scientists at Brookhaven National Laboratory have used neutron activation analysis to compare the rate of manganese metabolism in normal persons and in patients with Parkinson's disease before and after administration of various drugs. Similarities between Parkinsonism and manganese poisoning are being sought in a collaborative study between Brookhaven and the Catholic University of Santiago, Chile. Results thus far are inconclusive.

Man's dependence on vitamin B_{12}, a cobalt-containing compound, has been discussed above in relation to pernicious anemia. This vitamin is also important in protein metabolism, liver function and other metabolic processes. Yet its precise role needs further clarification, and in this connection the significance of cobalt requires additional study. Cobalt levels in blood are less than one part per hundred million—levels too low to permit accurate chemical determinations. At Texas A & M University, however, an activation analysis study is now in progress

that should be able to provide the needed data, even in vitamin-deficient patients. At this center a high-speed automatic gamma-ray spectrometer capable of analyzing 2,000 samples a day will permit the necessary large-scale surveying of blood and other biological materials.

Optical Emission Spectroscopy
In recent years it has become apparent that trace metals often may participate in biologic processes by serving as functional and structural components of enzymes. For example, fifteen zinc-containing enzyme systems have been identified and characterized, fourteen of them since 1954. Vallee and associates at the Peter Bent Brigham Hospital in Boston, have employed the method of optical emission spectroscopy to quantitate the trace metal in the enzyme system. Further studies of these highly purified metalloenzymes have led to important gains in understanding the mechanism of enzyme catalysis as well as the role of metals in physiologic and pathologic systems. The following are some examples of these studies.

It was shown that carboxypeptidase A of bovine pancreas contains one zinc atom per mole of protein. Further investigation demonstrated the importance of this zinc atom in the activity of the enzyme. If the zinc atom was removed from the protein there was concomitant loss of enzymatic activity, and when the zinc was replaced there was full restoration of activity. Moreover, if the zinc atom was replaced by a different metal a change in enzymatic specificity resulted.

Zinc was also shown to be a component of the active center of mammalian liver alcohol dehydrogenase, the enzyme which catalyzes the first step in detoxification of ethyl alcohol. Recently, this enzyme was isolated for the first time from human liver. It has been found that ethylene glycol also will serve as a substrate for human alcohol dehydrogenase and that it competes with ethyl alcohol for oxidation by this enzyme.

The observation that zinc is an important component of alcoholic dehydrogenase led to studies of zinc metabolism in patients with post-alcoholic cirrhosis of the liver. The studies showed that such patients had markedly lowered concentrations of zinc in the blood serum,

Counter employed with neutron activation analysis system at Texas A & M University. Samples are transported from reactor to counter by pneumatic tubes shown at top center. Counting then proceeds automatically, using computer methods.

significantly lowered concentrations of
zinc in the liver tissue, and abnormally
large quantities of zinc excretion
in the urine.

X-ray Fluorescence Spectroscopy
In 1960 Gofman at the University of
California, Berkeley, began to study the
occurrence and distribution of trace
elements in the blood by X-ray fluorescence. Using this method, 66 trace
elements can be measured in a single
blood sample with an accuracy of one part
in a million to one part in a hundred
million, which is between 100 and 1,000
times the sensitivity usually obtained
by conventional chemical methods.
Elements from phosphorus (atomic number
15) through uranium (atomic number 92)
have been measured by this method.
The approach differs from others in that it
provides a colligative study of many
elements rather than of one element at
a time. Measurements have been made on
blood samples from healthy persons as
well as from persons having schizophrenia,
monogolism, certain genetic disorders
of metabolism, and alcoholism. For
example, patients with familial xanthoma-
tosis (xanthoma tuberosum and xanthoma
tendinosum), an inborn error of fat
metabolism, were recently studied and
significant differences from normal
found in the blood serum concentrations of
phosphorus, sulfur, chlorine and zinc.

Chapter 2
Medical Therapy

Medical Therapy

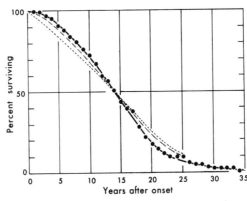

Survival curve for 297 patients with polycythemia vera who have been treated with phosphorus 32 shows that their median life expectancy is similar to those of diabetics treated with insulin and of pernicious anemia patients treated with vitamin B_{12}.

Injected or Ingested Radionuclides

Nuclear medicine came into existence when cyclotron produced radioisotopes and nuclear radiations became available in the United States in 1935. Early investigations with radiophosphorus and radioiodine in normal and leukemic animals made it apparent that the injection of certain radioactive compounds offered a method for selectively irradiating certain regions within the body. After experimentation with leukemic animals showed some selective localization of phosphorus 32 in leukemic tissue, radioisotopes were introduced into successful therapy in 1937 when a patient with chronic lymphatic leukemia was treated with sodium radiophosphate (P^{32}) at the University of California.

Since that time therapeutic uses of injected or ingested radioisotopes have become widespread. Phosphorus 32 continues to play an important role in the treatment of blood diseases. For example, over 25 years experience with sodium radiophosphate, given orally or intravenously, have resulted in the successful control of polycythemia vera, so that the life expectancy for these patients is now about the same as that for treated diabetic or pernicious anemia patients. Administration of radiophosphorus has also proven to be a simple and highly accepted means of inducing long term remissions in certain patients with chronic leukemia. Iodine 131, first used therapeutically in the United States in 1941, has continued to be important in the successful treatment of thousands of patients with hyperthyroidism. There are many other compounds containing various radioactive isotopes being widely used in the palliative treatment of several neoplastic and other diseases throughout the world.

Heavy Particle Beams

The advent of the first relatively large cyclotron in 1935, also led to consideration of the therapeutic use of heavy-particle beams. It was quickly discovered that such beams (neutrons) had a greater relative biologic effect (RBE) on normal and neoplastic tissue per unit of ionization than X rays or gamma rays (Table IV). New safety standards were immediately established for workers around the neutron sources, the permissible dose being set at one-tenth that allowed for X rays. Neutron beams were soon tried in cancer therapy, but the results were disappointing largely owing to the great amount of scattering and to lack of penetration.

Accelerator theory and practice advanced rapidly, however, and soon cyclotrons were capable of producing high-energy, heavy, charged-particle beams with many qualities of special value to biology and medicine. These included greater penetration, less scatter and less dependence on oxygen concentration (so important in the treatment of neoplastic tissue, which is relatively anoxic), in addition to a greater RBE per unit dose. It was also observed that under certain conditions a monoenergetic beam could be stopped abruptly in tissue with a great release of energy (Bragg peak effect) and that it was possible to perform "cutting" operations with this radiation. Thus it became possible to deliver radiation energy in relatively localized packages to great depths in tissue, with greater RBE in the desired area and relatively little radiation dose to nearby tissue.

In 1948 Bragg-peak irradiation was first used to treat successfully a mammary carcinoma in mice. The beam of high-energy protons was passed through the animal's body so that the Bragg peak provided localized radiation to a tumor on the opposite side. Several years of extensive animal studies followed. Then in September 1954 a beam of high-energy protons was used for the first time on a human, in this case to destroy the pituitary gland of a patient with advanced metastatic cancer of the breast. Beginning in 1957, a 910 MeV alpha-particle beam was employed.

When heavy-particle beams are used for pituitary irradiation the patient's head

Table IV
The early studies on the comparative effects of x-rays and neutrons on various organisms

Organism	Effect Measured	X-rays dose in r	Neutrons dose in "r"	X-rays/neutrons ratio (r/"r")
Drosophila Eggs	50% Hatching	180	87	2.1
Wheat Seedlings	50% Normal Growth	1,000	200	5.0
Normal Mice	Lethal Effect	800	200	4.0
Mammary Carcinoma	In Vitro 50% Takes	3,600	700	5.1
Fern Spores	50% Inhibition	52,000	21,000	2.5
Bacteriophage	50% Inactivation	20,000	11,250	1.8
Chick Embryo Fibroblast	Inhibition of Growth	105,000	45,000	2.4

Schematic representation in a tissue-like material of the dose distribution produced by several types and energies of radiation. Note that there is greater depth dose with less scattering in the case of the high-energy heavy particles.

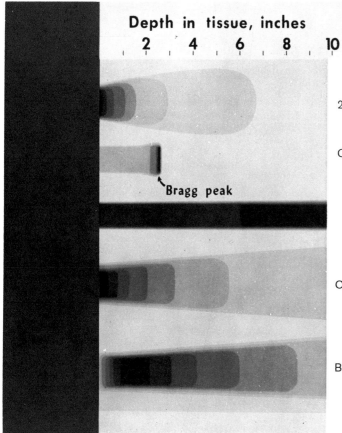

Depth in tissue, inches

2 4 6 8 10

200 kV X RAYS
HVL 2 mm Cu

CYCLOTRON
380 MeV alpha particles attenuated from 910 MeV

340 MeV protons normalized at 10 inches

Bragg peak

Co⁶⁰ GAMMA RAYS

BETATRON
22 MeV X rays

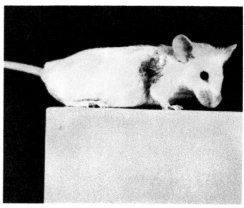

Results of an experiment done in 1948 when Bragg-peak irradiation was first used to treat an animal tumor. The heavy particle beam was directed to pass through the animal's body, the transplanted mammary tumor being on the opposite side of the body at the position of the Bragg peak. The upper animal was a control (untreated); the lower animal was treated.

52

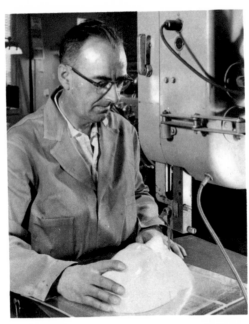

The cooled, formed sheet is removed, trimmed and then fitted with quick-release clamps to secure it to the rear half of the mask, which has been made in the same manner.

This shows the front and rear portions of the face mask.

To deliver a precise cyclotron beam to the pituitary gland, or to a brain tumor, the physician must position his patient's head with true alignment. Stereotactic equipment is sometimes used or construction of a plastic mask which will constrain the head with firmness. For each patient a plaster cast of the head and, from this, a positive plaster matrix are made. The facial half of this matrix is seen here on the Vacuum Forming Machine.

A sheet of polystyrene is laid over the matrix. The oven compartment will then be rolled into place to soften the plastic at 340° F. This requires but three minutes.

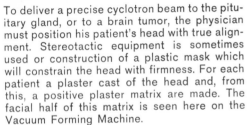

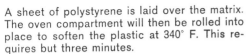

is held tightly by means of a specially fitted plastic mask. The patient may be continuously rotated with or without utilization of the Bragg peak, the beam being centered on the pituitary gland. The placement of the beam is aided by stereotactic methods. As a result the gland receives a high dose compared to surrounding structures, and each dose can have a greater biological effect due to dense ionization.

During the past ten years more than 300 patients have been treated in Berkeley, using this radiostereotactic technique, with or without the Bragg peak, to treat metastatic breast carcinoma, diabetic retinopathy, acromegaly, malignant exophthalmos, Cushing's disease, and brain tumors and Parkinson's disease directly.

Follow-up studies show that nearly all patients with acromegaly treated with heavy particle radiation to the pituitary gland have benefited both subjectively and objectively. Their headaches, excessive perspiration, lethargy and temperature intolerance have all been relieved. In addition, the typically coarse features of these patients have become less pronounced. Although it is assumed that these beneficial changes have occurred primarily in the soft tissue mass, structural and metabolic alterations have also been detected. Thus, head casts made before and after therapy have demonstrated a diminished thickness of the cortex while studies with radioactive calcium-47 in the whole body counter have shown changes in calcium metabolism.

Diabetes mellitus is one of the diseases modern medicine can control relatively well. With the extension of life brought about by treatment, however, some of the serious complications of the disease have become more prevalent and prominent. One of these is diabetic retinopathy, which can lead to blindness. Partial or complete pituitary destruction has been achieved with heavy particle beams in over 100 diabetic patients in an attempt to slow down the progress of retinopathy. Of 70 patients followed long enough for adequate re-evaluation, 29 have shown stabilization and 18 have shown improvement in vision and retinopathy.

Several patients with Cushing's disease (a condition associated with adreno-cortical hyperfunction often due to

This shows the patient on the treatment table in the cyclotron's medical cave. The completed mask now performs two functions.
1) with the aid of X-ray diagnostic equipment it allows accurate positioning of the patient, and assures that this alignment may be repeated on the following treatment days.
2) it transmits to the head the rotational movement that is required for the beam to enter from a wide angle. In this way the radiation is minimized at the skin while delivering maximum doses to deep tissue, in combination with the Bragg peak.

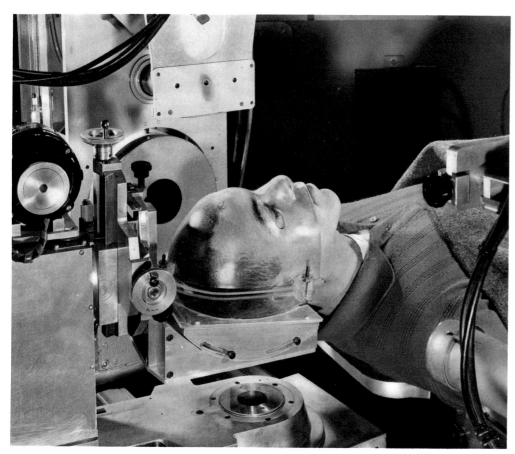

increased corticotropin produced by the anterior lobe of the pituitary gland) have been treated by heavy particle radiation to the pituitary. All have demonstrated marked improvement, evidenced by a disappearance of Cushingoid features and a return to normal of the altered metabolic processes.

The Bragg peak effect has also been utilized for direct irradiation of tumors, the first human patient having been treated in January 1960. Since that time heavy-particle beams from cyclotrons at the Lawrence Radiation Laboratory in Berkeley, Harvard University in Boston, and the University of Uppsala in Sweden have been used with encouraging results to perform hypophysectomies, to irradiate tumors directly, and to produce lesions in the nervous system for controlling the symptoms of Parkinson's disease.

From results thus far obtained, it appears clear that in the coming years heavy-particle beams from cyclotrons now available or soon to be available in many countries will be used increasingly in the treatment of certain neoplastic, metabolic and neurological diseases.

Patient in position to receive treatment with the 910 MeV alpha-particle beam from the 184-inch cyclotron at the Lawrence Radiation Laboratory. The head is held in a specially fitted plastic mask. The beam enters from the aperture at the left of the patient's head, and is centered on the pituitary gland with the aid of two diagnostic X-ray units. The table may be rotated during therapy, in conjunction with the Bragg peak.

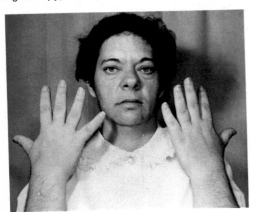

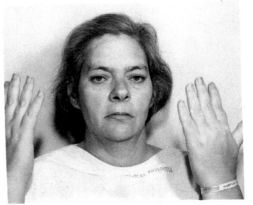

Two pictures of an acromegalic patient. The left was taken before therapy. The right was taken 4 years after therapy. She had received 5,880 rads of 910 MeV alpha particles (from the cyclotron in Berkeley) delivered to the pituitary gland in 12 days.

A patient with Cushing's disease before therapy (left) and eight months after therapy (right). She had received 8,500 rads of 910 MeV alpha particles delivered to the pituitary gland over an 11-day interval. As of mid-1964, nearly 5 years after therapy, her remission was continuing.

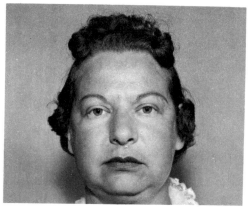
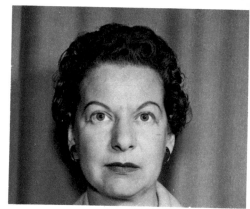

Patient in position to receive pituitary irradiation, using the 160 MeV proton beam from the cyclotron at Harvard University. Protons come from the beam pipe (arrow) and pass through a series of small holes which define the pencil-shaped beam directed to the patient's pituitary. The patient is rotated in the chair during the therapy. Closed circuit television (located at the extreme left center of the photograph) is used to monitor the patient. Final adjustments are being made prior to start of radiation.

These head casts of the acromegalic patient show the diminished thickness of the cortex 4 years after therapy.

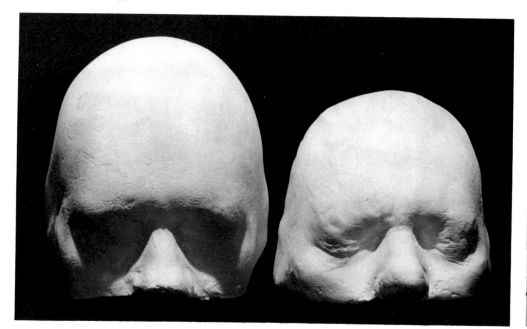
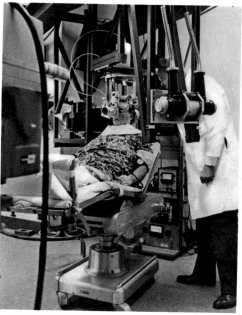

Implanted Radioisotopes

Internally implanted radioisotopes have
been successfully used at Argonne Cancer
Research Hospital and elsewhere to
supplant or supplement conventional
techniques for the selective removal of
tissue. The first such use was initiated at
Argonne in 1953 when concern about
the incompleteness of surgical removal of
the pituitary gland led to the suggestion
that it might be partially or totally
destroyed by placing point sources of
yttrium 90 within the gland. After
preliminary experimental work on monkeys,
the procedure was first undertaken on
humans in February 1954. It is now being
used throughout the world in the treatment
of metastatic breast cancers, diabetic
retinopathy, Cushing's disease, and
acromegaly. The isotopes are implanted,
as needles, seeds, or pellets, through a
needle inserted directly into the area
where irradiation is desired, thus delivering
a high dose to that point while sparing
the surrounding tissue.

Many considerations govern the
selection of suitable isotopes for such
applications. These include the type of
radiation emitted, half-life, cost, ease
of handling, and safety. Yttrium 90 and gold
198 have been the isotopes most often
used for pituitary implantation.

The tremor and rigidity of Parkinson's
disease have been alleviated at Argonne
Cancer Research Hospital by use of
a palladium 109 wire to create deep intra-
cranial lesions. Most recently a "nuclear
knife" consisting of a parent-daughter
mixture of strontium-90 and yttrium-90
hermetically sealed in the tip of a needle,
has been devised. It is implanted by
passing it through a surgically introduced
needle. Neurosurgeons have had much
success using this knife for destroying pain
fibers in the spinal cord to relieve pain.
It has also been successfully employed to
destroy the pituitary gland.

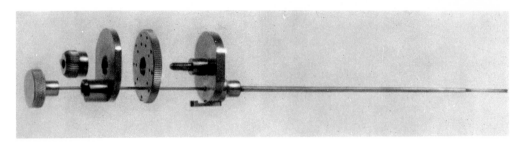

The needle used for implantation of yttrium-90
pellets into the pituitary gland. It is introduced
surgically, and the pellets are then passed
through it.

opposite:
X-ray picture showing introducing needle in
place and yttrium-90 pellets which it has deposited in the sella turcica, the bony area surrounding the pituitary gland.

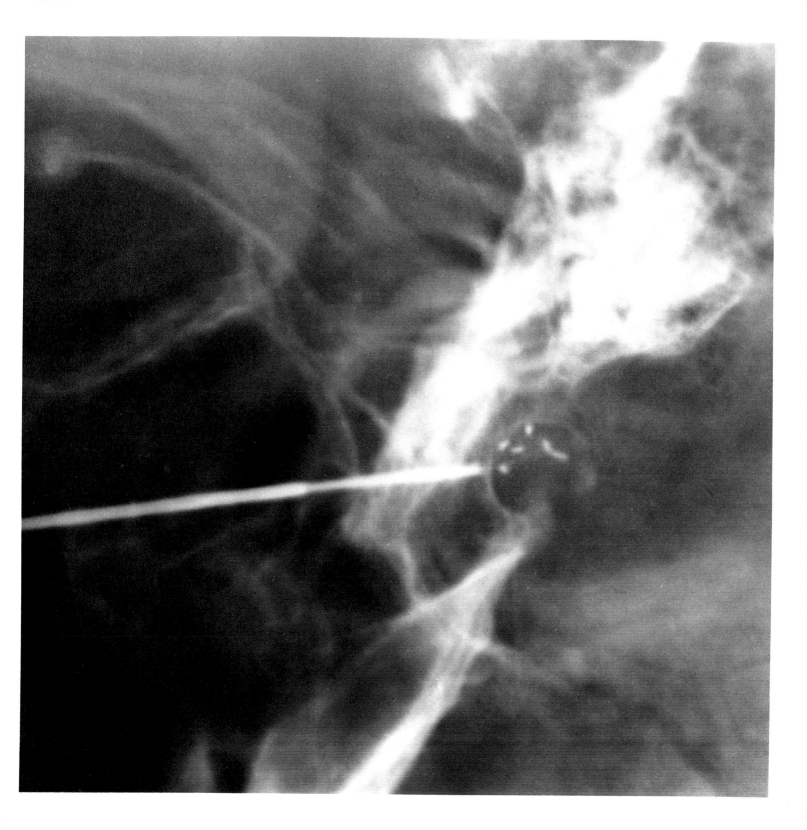

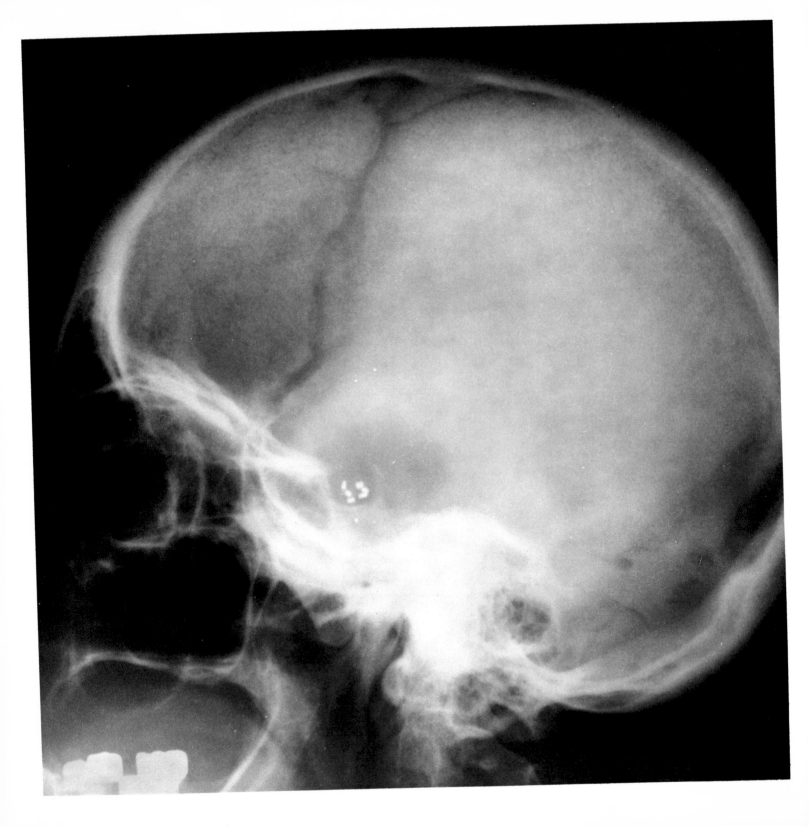

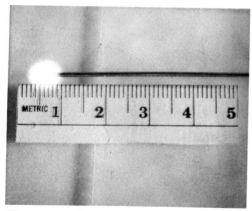

Photograph of the strontium-90 needle made under water. The bright spot at the tip is Cerenkov radiation.

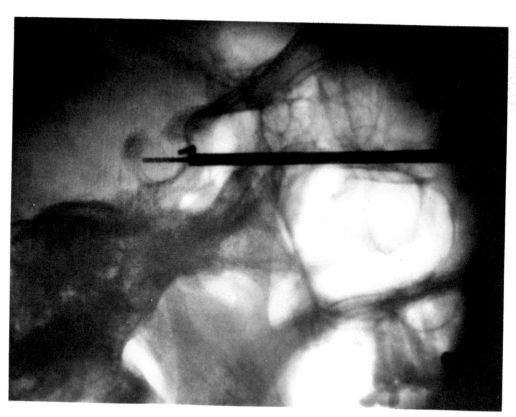

The strontium-90 needle being applied for the second time to the hypophysis (pituitary gland). In this lateral view one can see the screw plugging the hole made at the time of the first application.

opposite:
Another X-ray picture of the head showing the yttrium-90 pellets within the sella turcica.

The strontium-90 needle being applied to the spinal cord. The result will be a cordotomy which will relieve pain.

Teletherapy

As of January 1963 there were an
estimated 1600 isotope teletherapy units
in operation in hospitals and clinics
throughout the world, 475 of them being
in the United States. In addition there
are 200 high-energy (1 MeV and above)
X-ray and electron beam therapy
units, 80 of them in the United States.

These isotope units, which are sources
of high energy gamma rays, and super-
voltage X-ray units both have distinct advantages in certain situations over conventional X-ray apparatus. They can deliver
relatively higher doses to deep-seated
lesions while imparting relatively lower
doses to the skin and intervening tissues.
Thus, therapeutic doses can be administered routinely with little if any skin reaction.
Consequently the patient suffers much less
discomfort as a result of treatment. The
skin-sparing effect also makes it possible
to follow irradiation with classical surgical
procedures in cases where poor results
would be expected from either type of
therapy alone. The effects of such
combined therapy are currently being
evaluated in cancers of the lung, urinary
bladder, and breast, among others.

Another important advantage of these
methods of irradiation is that they make
it much easier for radiotherapists to deliver
effective doses. For instance, it is
commonly possible to employ single entry
portals or opposing fields rather than
laborious and time-consuming rotational or
multiple field approaches required with
conventional X-ray apparatus. In addition,
teletherapeutic methods have shown
encouraging results in some types
of tumors not easily reached by conventional X rays. These include tumors of
the oro-pharynx, urinary bladder, and
advanced cancers of the uterine cervix.
When comparing isotope teletherapy units
with those delivering high-energy X rays,
it is important to note that the latter
may require expert and expensive
electrical maintenance, whereas the
isotope units do not.

The majority of "reactor-produced"
isotope teletherapy units utilize cobalt 60 as
a source of gamma rays. One problem
with the use of cobalt 60 is its rather short
half-life, 5.3 years, which requires that
the source be strengthened every few years.

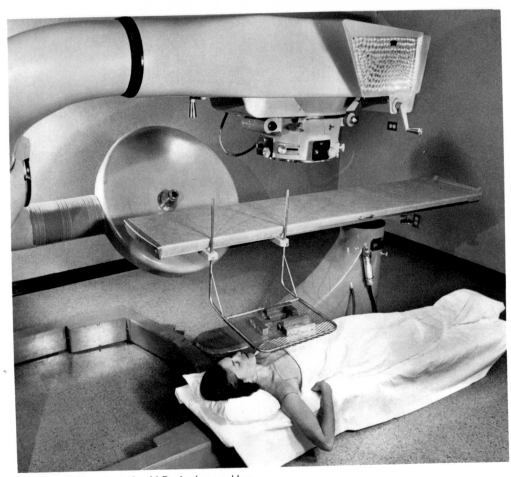

The cobalt-60 unit at the M.D. Anderson Hospital and Tumor Institute in Houston, Texas,
employs a 3,000 curie source. This unit has a
rotation suspension mechanism which allows
for rotation therapy about a stationary patient.
Several degrees of independent motion are
possible so that many different treatment positions may be accommodated. In this Figure a
patient is shown in position for therapy. Just
above her chest is an auxiliary diaphragm
which consists of an expanded metal tray on
which blocks of either tungsten or lead are
placed to absorb gamma rays and thus shape
the field of treatment. In this case they allow
for irradiation of the portions of the neck and
chest delineated by the lines visible on the
patient.

The control section for the cesium-137 unit. The
operator, protected from the intense radiation,
views the patient by means of angled mirrors.

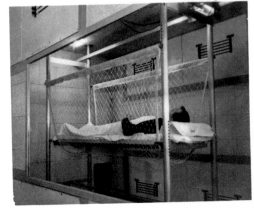

The use of cesium 137 (half-life 33 years) in place of cobalt 60 is therefore under study. The longer half-life of cesium 137 would ensure a nearly steady irradiation service over a period of approximately 20 years. However, cesium-137 sources have lower energy and poorer geometry. The total-body irradiation room at the Oak Ridge Institute of Nuclear Studies, completed in 1959, has eight 500-curie sources of cesium 137 placed in its walls. These sources are arranged to direct their beams to a high bed in the middle of the room. Even exposures to the entire body are made possible by beam shapes and filters. This unit is being used in investigational therapy.

Close-up view of 10,000 curie cobalt-60 source for a teletherapy unit with housing removed. The radioactive cobalt is ordinarily contained in the stainless steel capsules at the top. Below the capsules are shown the source centering mechanism and part of the pulley mechanism for lowering the source to its safe position at the bottom of a fifteen foot deep tank filled with water. This source can give radiation dose rates from zero to 10,000 roentgens per hour and can be used for research in medicine, biology, chemistry and physics.

The total-body irradiation unit at Oak Ridge Institute of Nuclear Studies. Eight 500-curie sources of cesium 137 are located in the walls of the room (knobs and grooves visible are associated with positioning controls of the sources).

Labeled Antibodies

Radioisotope-labeled antibodies provide a further means for irradiating tumor tissue. An interesting example is the labeling of the fibrin antibody which has been shown to concentrate in certain tumors. The mechanism involved here relates possibly to the fact that the tumor growth is destructive even to its own blood vessels and the supporting tissues, so that activation of the blood-clotting mechanism, which converts fibrinogen to fibrin, results. Substantial amounts of fibrinogen consequently are deposited in the tumor as fibrin which, in turn, is able to bind the injected circulating radioactive antibody to itself so that tumor tissue anywhere in the body is selectively irradiated.

Animals experiments using this technique have been consistently successful in curing some types of tumors. Bale and associates at the University of Rochester have performed clinical trials on some patients who have widespread cancer which was not responding to other therapeutic techniques. Scanning procedures there demonstrated that fibrin antibody labeled with iodine-131 was localized in metastatic brain tumor and in metastatic as well as localized bone sarcoma.

Head scan of a patient with brain metastases from a primary cancer of the lung. Iodine-131-labeled antibody was given (plus a fibrinolysin inhibitor). The picture shows that the labeled antibody was successfully localized in the lesion.

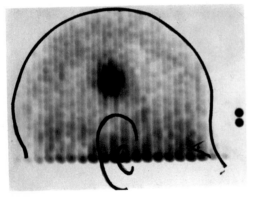

Preparation for Tissue Transplants

The early studies in 1937, which demonstrated some chemical protection against the effects of radiation by the use of estrogens in mice, have been followed by great advances in the understanding of the mechanism of radiation damage and associated tissue response. Although there has been little progress in finding adequate protection through the use of chemicals, anoxia does confer protection in experimental animals, and bone marrow transplants have been used quite successfully in treating radiation damage in isologous (highly inbred) animals and in identical twins. These findings have important implications in the field of tissue transplantation. One of the major problems in transplanting tissue in unrelated animals and man is the presence of an immume mechanism which causes rejection of the graft. Therefore, investigators today are seeking methods to suppress this immune mechanism.

This rejection of tissue homotransplants appears to be a function of lymphatic structures. In order to achieve successful tissue homotransplants, one must be able to ablate or modify this function. Because lymphatic cells are relatively more radiosensitive than most other body tissues, this can be accomplished in certain mammals by total body irradiation. However, in man this has not been the case, presumably because the amount of radiation required to suppress lymphatic tissue effectively is greater than would be tolerated by other radiosensitive human structures. Therefore, methods utilizing internally administered isotopes are being sought whereby lymphatic tissue may be suppressed selectively without seriously interfering with other vital organs or functions.

Studies on dogs and monkeys have demonstrated that yttrium 90, chelated with diethylene triamine pentaacetic acid (DTPA) and administered internally, offers some degree of selectivity in destroying lymphatic tissues. In addition, in five human patients with acute lymphoblastic leukemia there was some selectivity of this material in irradiating lymphatic tissue. Unfortunately, in this procedure the kidney receives too great an exposure to the isotope. Some other radioactive isotope or compound must be found which will be more selective in its irradiation of lymphatic tissue.

Utilizing another approach, radiocolloids (such as phosphorus-32 chromic phosphate) have been injected into the lymph fluid. These have shown a marked selectivity in irradiating certain lymph nodes, thereby suppressing the immune mechanism. With these techniques, some evidence of successful homologous bone marrow "takes" in dogs has been obtained, but the results are still preliminary.

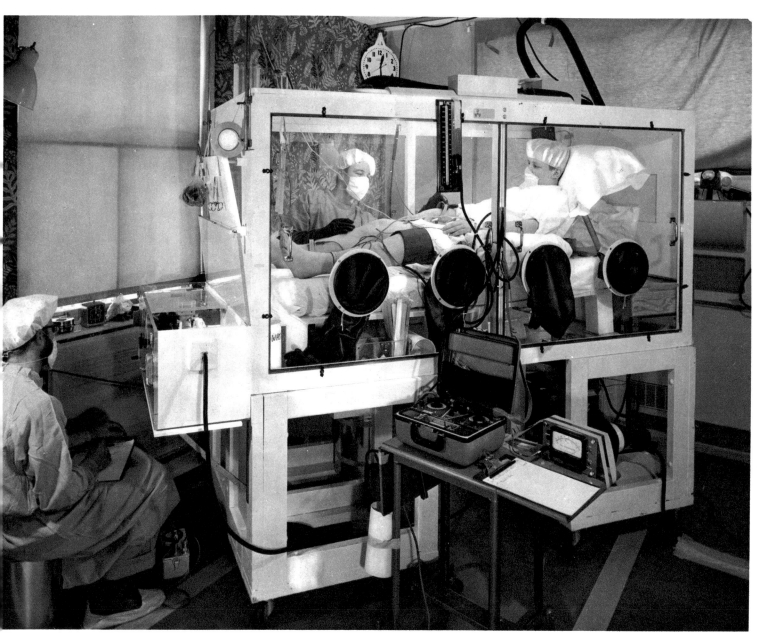

A patient with acute lymphatic leukemia is seen within the special enclosure which allows safe handling while he is receiving curie quantities of yttrium-90-DTPA. This is the internal radiation procedure used to suppress the immune mechanism of lymphoid tissue prior to giving the patient bone marrow transplant.

Veterinary Medicine and Animal Husbandry

The basic principles involved in the applications of radioisotopes to diagnostic and therapeutic procedures in humans are also applicable in veterinary medicine and animal husbandry. Radioisotope courses are now offered in many veterinary schools, and in these institutions veterinary clinicians are applying radio-isotope methods to the diagnosis and treatment of animal diseases.

Diagnostic and Research Studies

Iodine-131 thyroid uptake measurements are used in metabolic studies and for diagnosing thyroid diseases in various animals. Liver function in sheep has been studied with iodine-131-labeled Rose Bengal. A scintillation probe mounted over the liver detects the activity which is recorded by a ratemeter. Such studies have demonstrated the presence of biliary obstruction in this species.

Cornelius and Kaneko of the University of California Veterinary School at Davis studied red blood cell survival and iron metabolism in cows suffering from porphyria erythropoietica (a type of anemia). They used red blood cells labeled with carbon-14-glycine and iron 59 for these studies. The red cell survival time of porphyric cows was found to be only one-fifth that of normal cows. Their heme and red cell iron replacement rates were approximately three times greater than in normal cows. It was further found that an increased red cell replacement rate preceded the appearance of morphological evidence of anemia in the peripheral blood of these cows.

The red cell survival times of certain animals native to regions of high altitude have also been studied with carbon-14-glycine-labeled red blood cells. The mean survival times in two Himalayan tahr goats studied at sea level were 160 and 165 days respectively, as compared to an average of 125 days for domestic goats and sheep. Red cells in the guanaco (wild llama), also studied at sea level, had a mean survival time of 225 days. Such information contributes to an under-standing of adaptation to widely differing environments.

Trace elements are important to the health and well-being of animals. Consequently, just as in human studies, activation analysis has been employed to detect and quantify trace elements in animals. "Crooked calves", a disorder in which the affected calves have per-manently bent legs and/or twisted necks and spines, has been a serious and costly problem to some ranchers. Dyer, at Washington State University, used a nuclear reactor to irradiate samples of bone and tissue from both normal and malformed calves, and then employed a beta-ray spectrometer to measure the manganese content. He demonstrated that the manganese content in the normal calves was two to three times higher than in the malformed calves. Ranchmen have overcome this problem by feeding a well balanced mineral supplement containing manganese.

The value of the carbon 14 breath analyzer in studying the intermediary metabolism of carbon compounds in humans has already been discussed. This subject is also of interest in animal studies, and a breath analyzer has been developed for such use. Kleiber, at the University of California, Davis, devised an ingenious machine to aid in understanding metabolic studies performed in cows using tracer compounds. The hydraulic analog computer was constructed with the aim of studying theoretically the extent to which the tracer concentration versus time curves for various pools may be used to indicate pool sizes and turnover rates. Electronic computer techniques are now widely used in Biology and Medicine and also in Veterinary Studies.

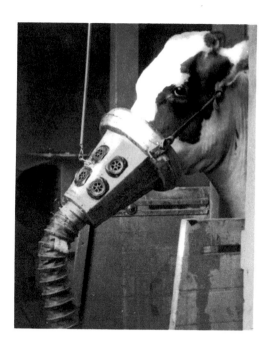

This shows a specially designed respiration mask used with the carbon-14 breath analyzer to measure the rate of oxidation to carbon dioxide of carbon-14-labeled compounds administered to cows.

This shows a transportable respiration apparatus that is used for metabolic studies on dogs, sheep, and other small farm animals.

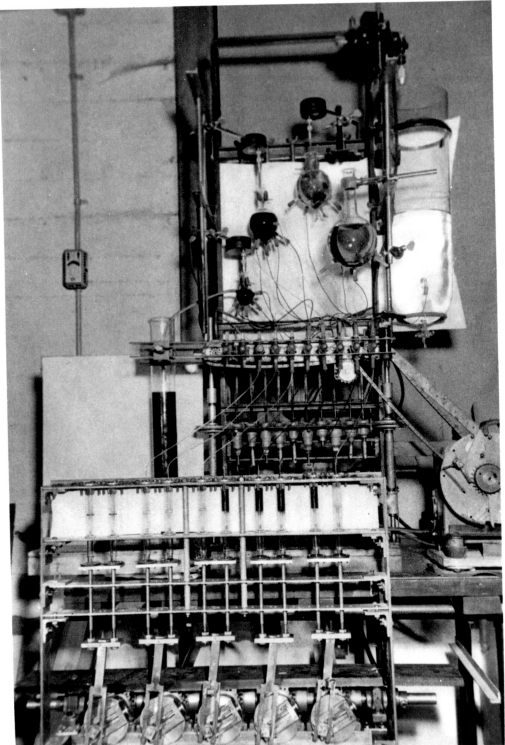

This is the hydraulic analog computer, devised by Kleiber at the University of California at Davis, which is used to simulate the conditions inside the cow with respect to pool sizes and turnover rates of carbon-14 labeled substances. The various flasks represent the relative pool sizes of the carbon dioxide in the blood, in the extracellular fluid, being produced in cells, and present in the skeleton. The flasks are interconnected by syringe pumps which control the mixing rates. Evans blue dye, representing the tracer which is injected into the animal, is injected into the circulatory pool and the concentration of dye in the various "pools" at specific times is determined by a spectrophotometric method. The results with the analog system are compared with those obtained by carbon-14 breath analysis in the cow. Compatible schemes may be studied further; non-compatible ones discarded.

The Bossy Nova Mark I, a 700-curies twin shield source of cobalt 60 developed at the Davis Campus of the University of California.

Milk Production

In addition to concern for the health and quality of domestic and farm animals, veterinary science is also interested in the production of important animal products of direct use to man. Since the early studies in the period 1937-1940, with isotopes of iron and calcium as related to milk production in cows, radioisotopes have played valuable roles in many physiological and biological studies which have provided knowledge which will lead to increased quantities and improved qualities of such products.

One important example is the study of milk production performed by Luick and Kleiber at the University of California Veterinary School in Davis. Before the advent of radioisotopes the only measurements possible related to food intake and milk output. Radioactive tracers have made possible the study of the intermediate steps involved in the metabolic pathway of milk production. Luick and Kleiber administered carbon-14-labeled organic precursors to cows and used the carbon-14 breath analyzer to determine the isotope content of the expired air. It had previously been thought that blood fat is converted to milk fat in the udder. These studies demonstrated that the plasma glucose (blood sugar) contributes more than 70% of the carbon required for glycerol synthesis and that milk fat glycerol is synthesized directly in the mammary gland of the cow. The finding that this entire process takes place in one discrete anatomical region has provided the basic information needed for further biochemical studies to analyze the mechanisms of production of the various milk components.

Another investigation concerns the effect of radiation on milk composition and production. For these studies the Bossy Nova Mark I, the 700-curie cobalt-60 source already mentioned, is employed. By means of the collimated ports it is possible to irradiate only one section of the udder. The milk collected from this unit may then be compared to that from the non-irradiated section, the latter serving as a control. So far no changes in milk production have been indicated in cows irradiated with doses up to 3,000 r.

Therapeutic Applications

The use of radioisotopes in animal therapy has not been very extensive. One example has been the strontium 90 probe for the successful treatment of various forms of skin cancer. One type, epithelioma of the eye, is found in about 3% of Hereford cattle. These cancers grow relatively slowly, and if treated early will respond to radiation therapy. If left untreated the cancer soon extends beyond the point of possible treatment and the animal must be destroyed. Strontium 90, which emits beta rays of low penetration, has proven to be a satisfactory isotope for use in irradiating the cancer without damaging the lens and deeper structures of the eye.

Cobalt 60 has been used in certain conditions in animals. Lameness, especially in race horses, has been treated by packing cobalt-60 sources around the animal's leg. This decreases inflammation and relieves the lameness. The Bossy Nova Mark I, a 700-curie cobalt-60 source, may be employed for this purpose. The collimated ports may be used to irradiate specific areas of the animal's body in investigative studies of the effects of radiation on metabolic processes.

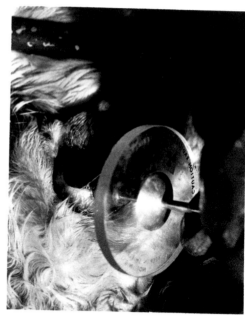

The strontium-90 applicator being applied to the cornea of a cow for treatment of an eye cancer. The technician wears lead-lined gloves and the plastic disc serves to further protect his hand from the beta rays emitted.

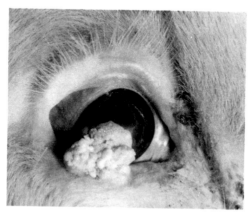

A cancer of the eye demonstrating the large amount of superficial tumor which occurs in some cases. This growth is first shaved down level with the cornea, and the strontium-90 probe applied to irradiate the growth.

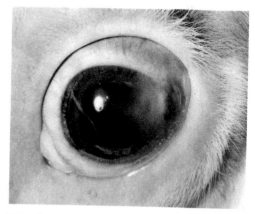

This shows an eye that has been successfully treated with the strontium-90 probe.

Chapter 4
Agriculture

Agriculture

One of the most imperative demands on science the world over is to find ways for increasing the productivity of agriculture. The need comes primarily from unprecedentedly rapid increases in population. At the same time there is an insistent demand for improved living standards on the part of most of the peoples of the world, a demand reinforced by rising levels of industrial production. Consequently, agricultural producers must not only feed ever-increasing numbers of people, but feed them more and better. The need cannot be met solely by expanding the acreage under cultivation; there is neither sufficient land nor agricultural manpower available for this. Significant increases in productivity are required.

As is well known, the United States has achieved very high levels of agricultural productivity. Much of the explanation for this is doubtless to be found in inherent richness in natural resources. But agricultural abundance in the United States has also been to a considerable extent man made. One must look in particular to four concurrent lines of development which have had important effects on agricultural productivity. These are:
1) the development of improved species and varieties of plants and animals;
2) improvements in soil and water management;
3) mechanization; and
4) control of plant and animal diseases and of pests.

To achieve the current level of productivity in United States agriculture, it was probably necessary to make advances in all of these four fields simultaneously. The fact that this occurred owed much to the early arrival of the industrial revolution in the United States. Thus, the chemical industry was available to implement improvements in soil management by providing vast supplies of appropriate fertilizers. The chemical and petrochemical industries also provided the needed quantities of pesticides, while the burgeoning machinery industry made large-scale mechanization possible.

Also of great importance in explaining the development of United States agriculture has been the fact that the active interest of universities and industry and the participation of Government have led to extensive agricultural research. From this research has come information leading to new varieties of plants and animals which are resistant to disease, and producible in large quantities. Research continues to be employed toward these ends and, lately, has been directed as well to the solution of a variety of auxiliary problems, such as how best to prevent spoilage of harvested crops during the marketing cycle, or when stored as surplus.

It should be understood that there are a host of individual inquiries contributing to the objectives of agricultural research. Many of the projects are being carried out by the use of conventional physical and chemical techniques. On the other hand, radioisotopes are being employed in an increasing number. Where use of radioisotopes is the technique of choice, it is frequently because they permit information to be obtained in less time, with greater ease, and with more accuracy than would be possible with other techniques. In some cases radioisotope techniques have provided information that would have been impossible to obtain in any other way. Practical agricultural applications of radiation sources have also been made.

In this chapter we will review first some of the more important recent uses of radioisotope tracers in agricultural research. Then there will follow a description of three applications of radiation sources which have been or can be of significant benefit in solving agricultural problems. These are the elimination of insect pests by mass release of insects made sterile by irradiation, the radiation disinfestation of grain, and the use of radiation to produce useful plant mutations.

Plant Nutrition Studies

Three major factors are taken into account in seeking the improvement of plant nutrition: environmental photosynthesis, i.e., making light and carbon dioxide available to the plant; water control, i.e., making available an appropriate carrier for nutrient transfer; and salt uptake, i.e., making plant food available in the proper form.

Curiously enough, although the present understanding of the mechanism of photosynthesis is due almost entirely to radioactive tracer research, the major practical application of the atomic energy program from the environmental photosynthesis point of view has been the development of micrometeorology. The concern over atmospheric pollutants has led the Atomic Energy Commission to develop highly sophisticated techniques for measuring wind velocities, temperatures, and air impurities, resulting in the accumulation of a vast amount of micrometeorological data. These data and techniques are now being used by the agronomist to select sites which provide optimum amounts of light and carbon dioxide, and to predict effects of meteorological changes on plant growth.

Water control has long been an empirical art with the farmer, and to a great degree still is. The moisture capacity of a particular soil is judged in a majority of cases by the farmer's practical experience. In some instances simple water tension analysis is used. Sophisticated techniques which rely on gamma or neutron scattering are employed very rarely.

It is in the study of salt uptake that radioactive tracers have had their greatest impact. It has been known for generations that nitrogen, potassium, and phosphorus are important plant foods. The general role in agriculture of all the elements in the periodic table has been determined empirically during the last fifty years. Investigations having to do with the optimum use of fertilizers, such as comparisons of fertilizer materials; determination of when it is best to fertilize, at what rate, and where fertilizer should be applied; and evaluation of the needs of various soils, have been underway for many years. Prior to the advent of radioisotope techniques, however, these determinations also had to be made empirically, based on observed growth responses and accompanying changes in the chemical composition of plants. Gathering of information was accordingly slow and inherently inaccurate. By contrast, radiotracer techniques have proved to be rapid, specific, and accurate.

In the late thirties and early forties, shortly after radioisotopes were made available, soil and fertilizer research with radioactive tracers began and soon the United States Department of Agriculture (USDA) made a variety of labeled fertilizers available on a national scale. They were rapidly and widely employed in a very large number of research investigations. In many cases the radiotracer technique confirmed the validity of fertilizer practices that had been developed empirically. In other cases they provided new information. One such example follows.

The California Cotton Experience

For some years attempts to grow cotton in some parts of the Tulare Lake Basin of Central California had met with consistent failure. Farmers in the area eventually were forced to shift to barley.

Because barley is a far less profitable crop for California producers, some growers tried cotton again. But now the soil, which had received nitrogen and phosphorous fertilizers to increase its barley yield, was even more unacceptable for cotton production.

At the instance of one large grower, agronomists at the California Chemical Company, under the leadership of Dr. George Hawkes, were retained to analyze the problem. Field trials were initiated and soil samples were sent to the USDA's Plant Nutrition Laboratory at Beltsville, Maryland. There, Dr. J. C. Brown, using radioactive tracer techniques, particularly with zinc 65, was able to obtain quick indications of nutrient activity in cotton plants grown in this soil. His determinations led to a rapid solution as follows:
1. A zinc deficiency was prohibiting successful cotton growth.
2. The soil suffered also from phosphorous deficiency, but adding phosphorous alone increased the zinc deficiency.
3. If zinc and phosphorous fertilizers were added together, iron deficiency would result in susceptible plants.
4. Hence, a combination of zinc, phosphorous, and iron fertilizers was required for successful cotton production.

Today high yields of cotton are being harvested from many hundreds of acres in the area. It is clear that radioisotope techniques of investigation were able to bring this about with much greater speed and precision than would have been possible with other methods.

Cotton fields in Tulare Lake region of California after application of zinc and phosphate fertilizer in proportions determined by radioisotope research.

Response of plants grown in Tulare clay to application of various nutrients as disclosed in research at U.S. Department of Agriculture's Beltsville Experiment Station.

Zinc: at left none, at right 97 parts per million. Tomatoes, okra, and kidney beans show markedly increased growth when zinc is added to Tulare clay.

Zinc: at left none, at right 97 parts per million. With other crops different effects show up. PI soybeans (top) developed iron chlorosis (yellowing) in both treatments. Two varieties of corn (middle and bottom) showed stunted growth from zinc deficiency (left) and iron chlorosis yellowing when zinc was added (right).

Zinc: at left none, at right 97 parts per million. Some crops are relatively unaffected by presence or absence of zinc. HA soybeans (top), wheat (middle), and barley (bottom) showed neither growth stunting nor iron chlorosis.

Phosphorus left to right:
0, 32, 97, and 161 parts per million.
As phosphorus is added to normal Tulare clay,
some crops are affected adversely (top to bottom): lespedeza develops severe iron chlorosis;
dill, cocklebur, and cotton show varying zinc
deficiency symptoms.

Zinc 97 parts per million throughout.
Phosphorus left to right 0, 32, 97, and 161 parts per million.
As phosphorus is added to Tulare clay to which zinc has also been added, the response differs widely for different plants (top to bottom): lespedeza still exhibits severe iron chlorosis; dill shows markedly increased growth; cocklebur shows moderately increased growth; cotton shows response to zinc but little response to phosphorus. A delicate balance of zinc and phosphorus fertilizers is required for successful cotton production.

Using Insects for Their Own Destruction

Insects pose a serious threat to mankind. They reduce crop yields and lower crop quality. They attack stored food, clothing, and animals. They carry diseases of man and animals. There are several thousand insects in the United States which cause damage in varying degrees. Several hundred of these are imported insect pests and disease carriers which routinely require the application of control measures.

One of the chief reasons for the considerable success achieved in dealing with insect problems during the past two decades has been the discovery of a number of insecticides, each capable of destroying a wide variety of insects. However, there are limitations to the chemical approach to insect control. The most serious of these is the development of insect resistance to insecticides and the potential hazards from insecticide residues.

Many new techniques have recently been developed. These include the use of biotic control agents and attractants, and the selection and breeding of crop varieties which resist insect attack. Another means of direct control is the self-eradication of insects by the rearing and release of sterilized males. This method has met with remarkable success in wholly eradicating the screw worm fly from the Southeastern United States, where it had been causing millions of dollars of damage to livestock each year.

The sterile male technique depends for its success on the presence of certain conditions: sexual sterility must be achieved without adverse effects on mating behavior; it must be possible to rear the insects in large numbers; the sterile insects must be readily dispersible in a manner which will bring them into effective competition with normal males; and the huge (even though temporary) increase in population brought about by release of the sterile males must create no serious harm to crops, animals, and man.

Although the sterile male technique was first suggested by E. F. Knipling in 1937, and although the screw worm fly was plainly an ideal subject, it took 20 years to bring the idea to successful practice.

As part of the U.S. Department of Agriculture's eradication program, livestock owners collect maggots or eggs from wounds and send them to laboratories for positive identification.

Screwworm larva, showing comparative size and screw-like appearance which gives the insect its name. Larvae tear away living flesh and often kill untreated animals. Grown larvae drop to ground and enter pupal stage in the soil. Flies emerge from pupa to begin new cycle about 21 days from egg stage.

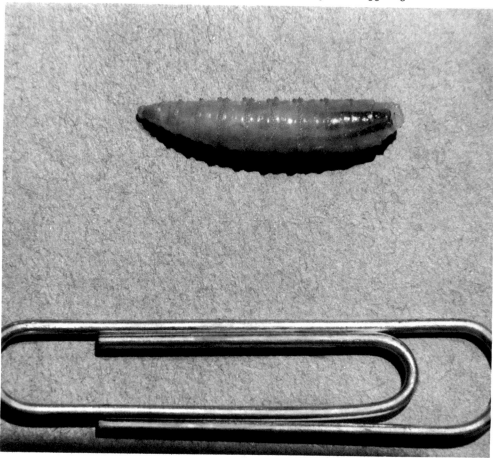

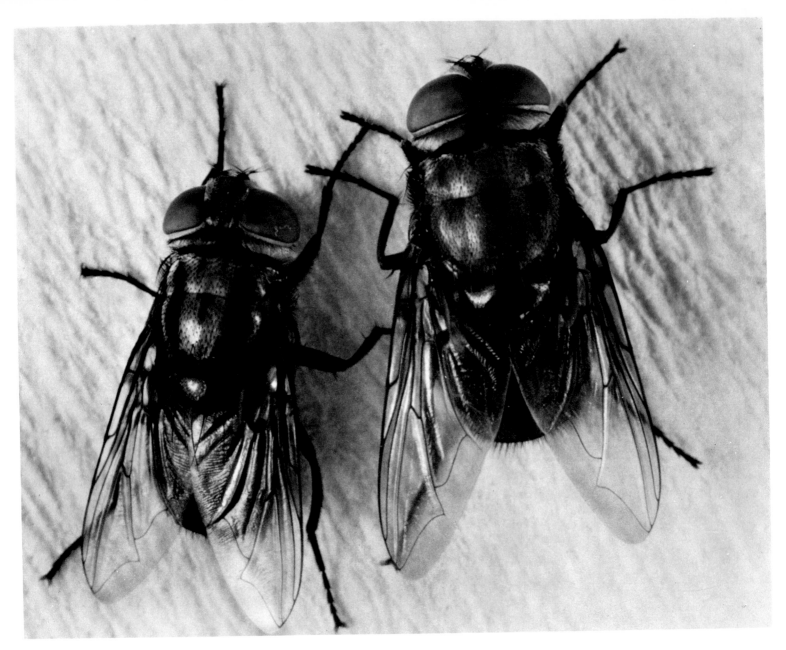

The screwworm fly has a bluish-green body and an orange-colored head. It is about twice the size of a housefly. Female (left) lays its eggs (about 250) on the edges of cuts or wounds of livestock and other warm-blooded animals, including man.

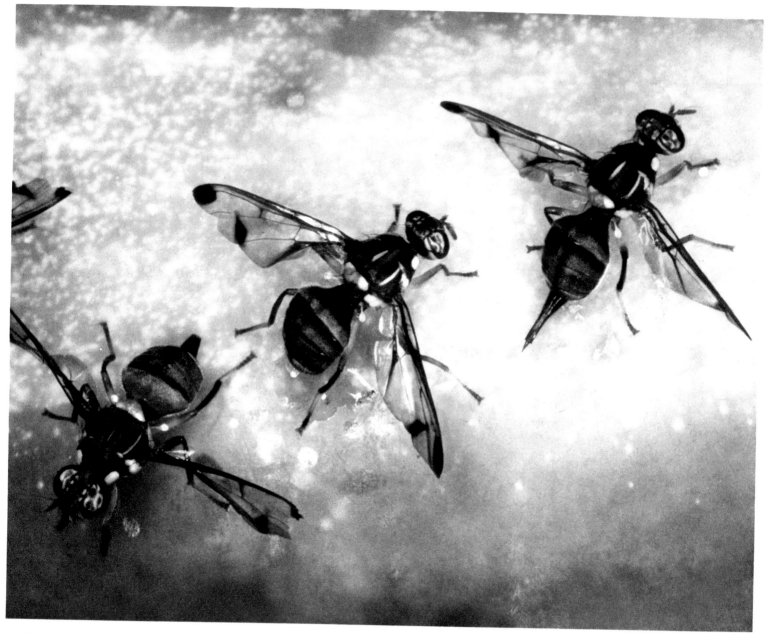

In the South Pacific, the melon fly causes
severe damage to melons, tomatoes, cucumbers, and other crops.

A milestone on the path to success was the 1954 experiment on the island of Curacao. Sterile male screw worm flies were released there at a weekly rate of 400 per square mile, three to four times the natural population, and completely eradicated the insect from the island.

Following the success on Curacao, a vigorous campaign to eliminate the screw worm from Florida began in 1958. An unused airplane hangar was converted into a factory. Six irradiators, each using 500 curies of cobalt 60, delivered the precise doses required for sterilization. Air-conditioned trucks transported each day's output of sterile insects to the air strips. The airplanes, provided with special equipment to break open each box as it was released, dropped about 200 to 3000 flies per square mile per week as they flew their courses. When the Florida plant reached its full capacity, it was rearing, irradiating, and releasing more than 50 million screw worm flies per week. More than 40 tons of ground whale and horse meat were required to feed the larvae and a fleet of 20 airplanes to handle the distribution.

The insect was eradicated in the southeastern portion of the United States in less than two years. The factory was then placed in standby condition. The Department of Agriculture maintains animal inspection and treatment sections at all crossings of the Mississippi river to prevent re-infestation. Thus, an investment of about 8 million dollars resulted in a saving of about 20 million dollars per year to the cattle industry in the southeastern United States. Without doubt this was one of the most extraordinary programs ever undertaken in the field of applied biology.

The success in Florida stimulated a demand for similar action in the southwestern United States and northeastern Mexico, which also suffer from heavy screw worm infestations. Accordingly, a survey was made in 1959 by the USDA in cooperation with State livestock officials in the southwest and representatives of the Republic of Mexico.

The screw worm problem in the southwest had several features which made it more difficult to deal with than it had been in Florida. For example, cold weather usually confined the overwintering screw

To produce fertile flies for mass egg production, screwworm pupae are placed in large screened cages which are kept in a warm dark room for about 7 days until the females are ready to lay their eggs. The cages are then moved to another room where a heated tray with a special meat mixture is placed in each cage. The females lay shingled batches of eggs near the medium. The trays with the eggs are then withdrawn, as shown, and placed for harvesting in a room kept cold to immobilize the adults.

Egg masses are collected, weighed and placed in small plastic containers where they hatch in about 12 hours. The larvae are then transferred to trays containing a starting food of ground meat and blood plasma. After 24 hours of feeding, the larvae are sucked, as pictured, into large vats. A warm mixture of ground meat, citrated whole beef blood, and water is piped into the vats.

Larvae feed for 3 to 5 days and then migrate out of the vat for the change to pupae, the next stage of their life cycle. Funnels on the sides of the vats direct the crawling larvae to water-conveying troughs in the floor under the grates.

The larvae pupate in trays of sawdust in approximately 16 hours. The trays are then emptied onto a machine that screens out the sawdust (pictured). The pupae and any remaining larvae are then passed under fluorescent lights. Larvae crawl away from the lights and are collected to complete pupation.

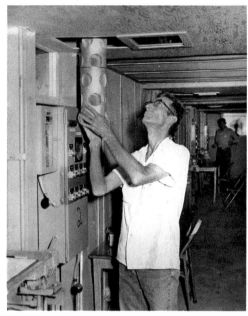

Exposure of pupae to gamma rays to cause sexual sterilization is handled by remote control. Aluminum canister containing about 18,000 pupae is placed on hoist and manipulated into one of the cobalt 60 chambers. After exposure to about 8,000 roentgens the canister is removed and conveyed to the packaging room.

Trays of pupae marked with pupation date are stacked on racks and held in a dark room at 80 degrees F and about 95 percent humidity for 5½ days before being sexually sterilized. Here an attendant examines the pupae's color, which changes from light red to black as they mature.

This assembly line packages 50 cartons of irradiated pupae per minute. The cartons are automatically assembled, filled, and closed. Then they are placed on trays and stored in portable racks for delivery by truck or plane to distribution centers.

worm population in the southwest to the southern half of Florida. Consequently, once destroyed, this population could not be reestablished by migration from the north, and the Gulf of Mexico and unsuitable climate for overwintering of screw worms in the states between Texas and Florida prevented reestablishment of the insect in Florida.

There are no similar barriers to prevent screw worms from moving freely throughout Northern Mexico. Consequently, it is necessary to develop and establish an artificial barrier through quarantine measures so as to prevent reinfestation of Southwestern areas freed of screw worms. Moreover, it is likely that reinfestation by flight will continue to occur so that release of sterile males will have to be repeated from time to time. A further difficulty is that the screw worm overwintering area in Texas and New Mexico is larger than it was in the Southeast. The terrain, climate, and vegetation of the two sections of the United States also differ vastly.

In spite of these relatively adverse features, information from the 1959 survey and from other sources indicated that the sterile male technique would be likely to succeed in virtually eliminating screw worms from the southwest area. Accordingly, in June 1962 a plant for rearing sterile screw worm flies was completed in Mission, Texas. In early 1964 the plant was in full operation, and release of sterile males was in process.

The screw worm fly precedent has inspired workers in the United States and in other countries to investigate the possibility of using equivalent methods to control many other varieties of pests. These include the oriental, melon, Mediterranean, and Mexican fruit flies; the pink bollworm and boll weevil; the sugar cane borer; the European corn borer; the gypsy and codling moths; the tsetse fly; and the anopheles mosquito.

In the case of the melon fruit fly, extensive tests by the USDA, under the direction of L. F. Steiner, have already yielded successful results.

The problems in the islands of the Pacific are considerably different from those in the United States, and the successful conclusion of the Hawaiian group's work was not without its difficulties. One problem was that both sexes of the fruit fly mate several times. During fruiting seasons in favorable areas the weekly emergence may exceed 100,000 flies per square mile. In addition, these fruit flies are known to travel distances ranging from 25 to 45 miles, and have made sustained overwater flights of 12 to 40 miles. Thus, very high rates of release of sterile flies, coupled with supplemental suppressive measures, were needed. One fortuitous circumstance was that sterile fruit flies could be reared in Hawaii at very reasonable cost (about $130/million flies). The large numbers of flies required to maintain high release rates made it economically impractical to segregate the flies by sexes, but this was no great disadvantage since sterile female flies did not seriously damage the fruit. Another serious problem was that when releases were made from the air, prop turbulence from the plane caused some of the boxes to disintegrate.

The Pacific island of Rota, a 33 square mile island in the Mariana group, was selected for tests on the melon fruit fly. This island is small enough to permit the economical treatment of an entire area of infestation with the available research resources, and the nearest land, Guam, is 37 miles away—far enough to greatly reduce chances of reinvasion by flight.

The first releases of sterile flies were made in the latter part of 1960 and throughout early 1961 at a rate of about 4 million flies per week. Although there appeared to be some reduction in melon fly infestation in January and February of 1961 when the wild fly population was very low, this advantage was soon lost, and there was no substantial reduction in infestation. Furthermore, the farmers expected that the scientists would control the fly for them, and neglected to use any pesticide control measures; thus the natural population increased to higher levels than would ordinarily occur.

In September 1962 the test was repeated. Before the first release of sterile flies, workers sprayed the borders of producing farms three times with bait sprays to reduce the wild fly population by 75 percent. Sterile flies were both dropped from aircraft and released from cages on the ground. Four to ten million sterile flies were released weekly until

the total released reached 180 million. Within three weeks the sterile flies outnumbered the native fly population by a ratio of 13 to 1. By early December 1962 the ratio reached 50 to 1, and by January 1963, 100 to 1. Scientists on Rota have not detected any melon fly maggots in watermelons, pumpkins, or cucumbers since December 26, 1962.

Work on the medfly is still continuing in Hawaii and at the Inter-American Institute of Agricultural Studies in Turrialba, Costa Rica. Work on other insects is proceeding in other parts of the world.

One concludes that, although the rearing and release of sterile insects method is not the final answer to insect eradication for all major insect pests, it certainly deserves serious consideration where conditions needed for its success seem to be present.

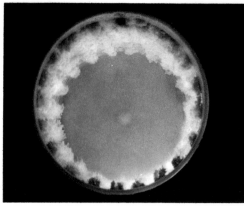

The melon fly and oriental fruit fly insert their eggs through pin holes in plastic ice cream cartons. Many thousands of eggs can be collected in a carton.

Tiers of portable cages used for production of fruit fly eggs at the United States Department of Agriculture's laboratory in Hawaii.

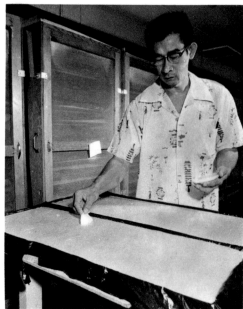

Fruit fly eggs are placed in trays on dehydrated carrot, a rearing medium. After hatching, the fly maggots complete their development in the carrot medium.

The pupal, or resting, stage of the tropical fruit fly, which resembles a grain of wheat, is the most convenient one to irradiate. The photograph shows many thousands of pupae, which have just been sterilized in Honolulu, being placed in trays prior to air shipment to the test site in the Mariana Islands. The aerated shipping container is shown in the background.

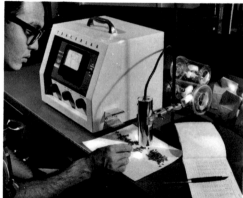

After the flies are recovered in traps a geiger counter is used to identify those tagged with radioactive phosphorus. This gives information on dispersal and also on the number of sterile insects which would have to be reared and distributed in order to over-flood natural populations.

After attachment to the arm of a hoist, the canister containing many thousands of pupae is inserted into the chamber in the lead cask (background), which contains radioactive cobalt. Adult flies emerging from the treated pupae are sterile.

Disinfestation of Grain

Each year the loss of stored wheat in the United States because of insect infestation represents a value of nearly $300 million. Some of the product is destroyed so that it cannot be used at all. Other parts are lowered in quality so that only limited use is possible, resulting in substantial reductions in value.

Considerable success in reducing infestation losses has been obtained through the use of pesticides, which are constantly being improved. There are legal restrictions on their use, however, because many of the pesticides tend to be toxic to humans. A widespread search is under way for effective pesticides which will be either non-toxic or low in toxicity.

At the same time, increasing attention is being given to the possibility of using some form of radiant energy for disinfestation. The use of high frequency sound, electrons, and gamma rays have all been considered.

Certain criteria have been established for successful disinfestation treatment against which proposed methods tend to be evaluated. It is considered, for example, that the treatment should have an enduring effect and that it should leave a low residue hazard. It must be economical and easy to apply. It must be effective against a wide variety of insect species. Since the rates of insect activity, feeding, development, and reproduction increase with temperature and moisture, the method should not be sensitive to these factors. It should not affect the germination of grain nor make the grain undesirable or disagreeable to handle in commercial channels. Finally, it must not have any adverse effect on the odor, grade, flavor, or baking qualities of the grain.

The extent to which alternative forms of radiation meet these criteria has not been fully determined, but there are promising auguries. A relatively low dose of radiation is sufficient to sterilize or kill a wide variety of insect pests. Such doses produce no effects on the grain which make it harmful for human consumption. (Evidence of this is found in the approval in 1963 by the U. S. Food and Drug Administration of radiation treatment of grain.) Nor do disinfecting doses impair the nutritive value of cereals. Electrons and gamma rays will add no residue and can be designed into a continuous and automatic operation.

There is still need, however, to demonstrate on an effective scale that radiation treatment will not adversely affect the grade, odor, flavor and baking qualities of grain, and that it can be economically competitive with other forms of treatment.

To help clear up the lingering uncertainties, the USAEC has proposed the construction of an irradiation facility for studies of insect control in grain and other commodities. This facility would be made available to the USDA for use in cooperation with industry. The program now proposed would include studies of the effects of radiation on insect populations in various commodities, the effects of radiation on commodity quality, the effects of radiation on different insects at various stages of their development, and comparisons of irradiated and fumigated grain. The facility is of such a design that it can be scaled up to provide cost comparison data.

Mutation Crop Breeding

The major portion of the human diet is provided by a relatively few families of crops. The cereal grains, together with the tubers, furnish the bulk of carbohydrates. A considerable portion of the protein comes from livestock feeding on grass and legume forages. Most of the remaining foods are legumes, leafy vegetables, and fruits.

All of the basic crop families were cultivated in neolithic times. Today thousands of variants of each are known. The usefulness of many crops is due to man's diligence in sorting out and preserving the more interesting or profitable variants. In modern times this practice has developed into the science of plant breeding, which can be defined as the experimental modification of gene frequencies in plant populations.

Evolutionary forces which influence gene frequencies include spontaneous mutations, gene migration, and the consequences of hybridization, selection, and chance. Spontaneous mutations occur so infrequently that it is not usually considered practical to await the appearance of desirable ones. Consequently, the conventional methods of plant improvement stress selection, and where necessary hybridization, in order to accomplish a favorable shift in gene frequency. These methods have been enormously successful in the United States in developing crops of high yield, resistance to disease, and ability to accommodate to special regional circumstances. Further successes are to be anticipated.

Quite another way of providing a supply of variants is "mutation breeding", which involves a deliberate effort to induce desirable hereditary changes. Radiation is an important tool for this purpose.

Efforts are being made to use radiation for mutation breeding in order to develop methods of treatment that will increase the frequency of desired mutants and reduce undesirable effects. For example, experimental evidence indicates that densely ionizing radiations, such as fast neutrons, produce a higher proportion of mutants and chromosome breaks per amount of reduction in plant growth than sparsely ionizing radiations, such as

gamma rays.

Among factors known to influence the sensitivity of an organism to radiation are the volume of the nucleus and chromosomes, the duration and stage of the cell cycle, the age of tissue, and the genotype. Environmental factors, principally moisture, oxygen, conditions of storage, and temperature, have also been found to influence the genetic effects of radiation, and these are of potential importance in practical application since they afford an opportunity for additional control over the mutation process. However, these environmental factors during irradiation influence the response in plants grown from seeds exposed to radiation of sparse ion density and have little or no effect in modifying responses to treatments with densely ionizing radiations.

The techniques for producing mutants in most cases involve the irradiation of seeds. For trees and vines which are propagated asexually the technique is to grow the tree in a radiation environment and detect and remove mutant cuttings.

Among the most successful applications of mutation breeding with radiation have been the development of crown rust-resistant oats, a tough hulled and spot disease-resistant peanut, a wide variety of new ornamental flowers and plants, and a new variety of pea bean. The latter development involves an interesting story which is worth narrating in some detail.

The Michigan Pea Bean Story
In 1941 C. F. Genter and H. M. Brown of Michigan State University reported on the effects of varying X-ray dosages applied to the seed of Michelite, a vine-type of navy or pea bean, and then the dominant type being produced in Michigan. Many different types of mutants were produced but none was mentioned at that time as being of any agronomic value. Nevertheless, in the same year, Professor E. E. Down, also at Michigan State, planted progenies from this material to insure that no valuable variants were being overlooked. A mutant bush or non-vining type of bean, smaller than Michelite and maturing about 12 days earlier, was found. By cross-breeding and selection, Professor Down was able to increase the size of the bush.

In 1948 the bean breeding work at the

Seed of the vine-type variety Michelite (right) was X-rayed and a bush mutant (left) recovered that matured ten days earlier.

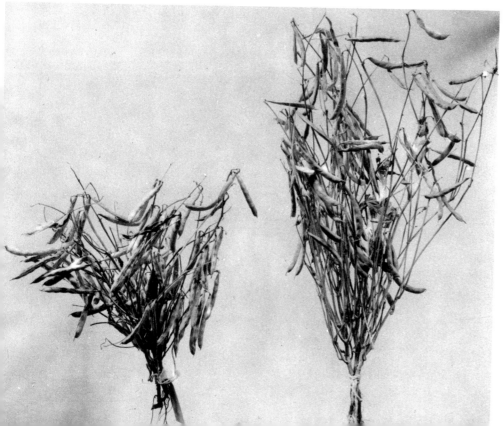

The bush mutant (left) was then crossed to Michelite and a selected offspring crossed with an anthracnose-resistant parent, resulting in production of a taller, anthracnose-resistant bush, Sanilac (right).

Michigan Agricultural Experiment Station was made a cooperative program with the U. S. Department of Agriculture, and Dr. Axel L. Anderson of the USDA joined Prof. Down. It occurred to the two scientists that cultivation of the bush type of bean might have a distinct labor-saving advantage in that it might be possible to harvest it by machine in one operation without prior pulling by hand. Moreover, this might make it possible for the beans to escape the serious damage which occurred when pulled beans were left in the fields several days to dry. (During the drying period seasonal rains and foggy weather frequently produced mold infestations which blemished the seed in the pod.)

This reasoning encouraged Down and Anderson to cross the mutant host with other varieties to improve the strain. By the mid-1950's several additional advantages had become apparent. The mutant tended to escape serious damage from white mold during the growth period because of better air movement resulting from its bush habit. In addition, it matured more uniformly than did the vine bean and had a much better yield.

The desirable characteristics of the mutant bean were retained in the breeding program, which resulted in the development in 1956 of a variety called Sanilac. In addition to the advantages previously noted for the new mutants, Sanilac proved to be resistant to fungus and wilt diseases which afflicted the Michelite variety; moreover, it outproduced Michelite by six bushels per acre, or approximately 20 percent.

Sanilac gained rapidly in acceptance. Whereas in 1956 and 1957 it was used only to grow foundation seed, in 1959 it constituted over one-fourth, and in 1962 eighty percent, of the bean acreage in Michigan.

In 1959 and 1960 Michelite fields were heavily damaged by disease, while Sanilac fields escaped. This fact, plus the greater yield of Sanilac, has led to estimates that upwards of $4,000,000 were saved to the farmers of Michigan in 1959, and about $5,000,000 in 1960, by virtue of their cultivation of Sanilac.

The breeding program which resulted in the development of Sanilac in 1956 also gave rise to other variants, which, because of special disease-resistant qualities, may in time replace Sanilac. These include the variety called Seaway, made available to bean growers in 1960, and one called Gratiot, made available in 1963. By 1962 Seaway already constituted 5% of Michigan bean acreage.

Recent "Radiation-Induced" Varieties Released in the United States

Mutant	Advantages	Year Released	Mutagen
Sanilac bean	Erect type of growth; disease resistance	1956	X ray
Seaway bean	Erect type of growth; disease resistance	1960	X ray
Gratiot bean	Erect type of growth; disease resistance	1962	X ray
Florad oats	Disease resistance	1960	Thermal neutrons
Alamo X oats	Disease resistance	1961	X ray
NC4 X peanut	Tougher hull	1959	X ray
Pennrad barley	Better winter hardiness	1963	Thermal neutrons
Yukon 1 carnation	Fewer petals; holds longer	1962	γ ray

Sanilac beans (left) and Michelite (right) in an
experimental field.

Harvesting Sanilac bean. Because of bush
characteristics machine harvesting is possible,
whereas the vine-type Michelite had first to be
hand pulled.

Chapter 5
Destruction of Bacteria in Food and Medical Supplies

Destruction of Bacteria
in Food
and Medical Supplies

The destruction of bacteria by radiation is a phenomenon that is extremely complex and not well understood. It probably involves the production of extensive genetic damage and, in addition, direct effects on cell cytoplasm.

Different types of bacteria differ widely in their radiation sensitivities; in some species virtually all organisms in a culture are killed by 400,000 rads; 4,000,000 rads are required to do this in other species. Just as in heat sterilization, when bacteria are irradiated the population is decreased exponentially so that it is theoretically impossible to kill all. Nevertheless, there is an effective sterilization dose which reduces to a commercially acceptable level the probability of any bacteria remaining viable.

The primary factor, in addition to the nature of the species itself, which influences the radiation sensitivity of bacteria is probably the duration and stage of the cell cycle at the time of irradiation. For example, bacteria will be more resistant in the spore form than when in an actively dividing state.

Environment plays a very important indirect role. Particularly important in promoting radiation sensitivity are the presence of water and oxygen. On the other hand, if the medium is chemically or biologically inadequate for bacterial growth, the organism will be relatively insensitive.

An extensive amount of empirical knowledge has been accumulated by research in radiation bacteriology. Two areas in which applications are being and have been developed are the radiation preservation of food and the radiation sterilization of medical supplies.

Food Preservation

The world hunger problem requires not only that ways be found to increase the productivity of agriculture, but that improved methods be developed for the preservation of available food stocks. Food spoilage is caused both by direct chemical and physical changes and by the action of microorganisms, the latter being the chief cause of food becoming inedible.

The perishability of foods has had serious effects in denying (except perhaps at prohibitive prices) certain foods to certain markets. For some localities this has caused a deficiency in the nutritive value of diets, particularly in those tropical countries where meat is scarce. In many more instances it has limited the variety and attractiveness of diets, even within the United States where in interior localities fresh fish is virtually unobtainable. From the standpoint of producers and those in the market chain, the perishability of foods has had severe economic consequences through restrictions of markets or heavy spoilage losses.

Refrigeration and canning have, until now, been the chief methods used for food preservation. Recently there has been widespread interest throughout the world in also using ionizing radiation for this purpose in the belief that under certain circumstances it may have economic or other advantages.

In the United States the USAEC supported research in this field as early as 1947-1948. The first major effort in this country, however, was that instituted by the U. S. Army's Quartermaster Corps in 1953. The object was to provide troops with more nourishing, palatable foods through a supply system which would not depend on refrigeration. A broad research and development effort was started in universities, non-profit institutions, and private industry, the main emphasis being on the use of sterilizing doses. Over 100 foods have been subjected to microbiological, chemical and physiological studies. Organoleptic characteristics (flavor, appearance, odor, etc.), packaging, dosimetry, and related subjects have also been investigated. The following are among the conclusions reached:
1. It is possible to sterilize, that is, effectively destroy all living organisms in any food, by the use of radiation.
2. The effect of sterilizing doses of radiation on the nutritive value of foods is a minor one, comparable to that caused by thermal processing.
3. There is no evidence of toxicity attributable to the radiation process.
4. All food products undergo some degree of flavor change at the sterilization dose. Foods vary in this respect—the flavor of milk products changes markedly, that of meat and fish moderately, and that of cereals and bread hardly at all.
5. Pasteurization (partial sterilization using lesser doses) results in far less flavor change than sterilization.

Progress has recently been made in retaining flavor at the sterilization dose by irradiating at very low temperatures (liquid nitrogen temperatures). Apparently the free radicals that react to produce off-flavors can be immobilized at these temperatures and dissipated harmlessly by controlled thawing. This technique has been particularly successful in the treatment of meats. At room temperature irradiated beef is normally among the most radiation-sensitive of meats. Low temperature irradiation, on the other hand, produces sterile steaks and roasts of acceptable flavor, odor, and texture, and indeed seems to have the additional effect of tenderizing the meat.

As part of the Quartermaster Corps program it was at one time planned to construct a pilot plant at Stockton, California. However, in the autumn of 1959, when it appeared that technology had not advanced to a point where a pilot plant was warranted, it was decided to build instead a facility to support further research. A research laboratory for food irradiation was accordingly constructed at Natick, Massachusetts. It has a 1.1 megacurie cobalt source, as well as an 18 kw variable-energy linear accelerator capable of providing electrons at energies up to 24 MeV.

In March 1960 the responsibilities for the U. S. Government's work on food irradiation were divided. The Quartermaster Corps was to continue its work on sterilization aimed at improving rations without refrigeration. The Atomic Energy Commission undertook to work in the low dose or pasteurization field, which had

Steaks being partially pre-cooked to inactivate enzymes prior to irradiation at U.S. Army Quartermaster Corps laboratory at Natick, Massachusetts.

Partially pre-cooked steaks being sealed in cans.

Cans containing partially pre-cooked steaks are placed in aluminum box (left) which is then conveyed into radiation cell.

Food is exposed to radiation from 1.1 million curie cobalt 60 source shown at bottom of storage pool. Source consists of two rows of tubes, 49 per row, containing a total of 392 encapsulated rods of cobalt 60.

been shown to offer the most immediate promise for commercial success.

The Army program has already had a striking success. On February 8, 1963, the U. S. Food and Drug Administration (FDA) cleared irradiated canned bacon for public consumption—the first radiation-sterilized food cleared by health officials of any nation. The bacon was sterilized by the gamma rays of cobalt 60 at a 4.5 megarad dose. After it was stored at 70°F for over two years, taste panels could detect little or no difference between it and fresh bacon.

On August 23, 1963, the FDA also approved, on petition by Dr. Lloyd Brownell and others at the University of Michigan, the public consumption of radiation-disinfested wheat and wheat products. Other petitions pending before the FDA request clearance for white potatoes (Army), oranges and lemons (Army and AEC), and materials used for packaging irradiated foods (AEC).

An alternative source of radiation to be used at the Natick facility is this 18 kw variable energy linear accelerator which will provide electrons at energies up to 24 Mev.

Preservation of fish.

One of the applications being studied in the AEC's part of the program which appears to have considerable promise is the radiation preservation of fish. It is interesting to consider in some detail the present trends in harvesting trawl fish, and to speculate on how they might be affected by this new preservation method. The discussion will be limited to practices in the New England area, whose trawl fisheries now produce nearly 70 percent of the domestically-produced fresh and frozen fish consumed in the United States.

Trawl-caught fish are those species taken by otter trawl gear, which in New England waters include haddock, cod, ocean perch, pollock, flounder, whiting, hake, and many others. There has been little change in the handling of trawl fish caught in New England trawlers in the past 50 years. When landed aboard the vessel, the fish are preserved in ice. The ground fish, such as cod, haddock, and hake, are generally eviscerated prior to being iced in the vessel's hold; ocean perch, whiting, and other smaller fish are refrigerated whole.

Fish can be kept for only a limited time in the fresh state, and popular species, such as haddock, cod, and ocean perch, are of unacceptable quality after being

Samples of food as they will be placed for accelerator irradiation.

stored in ice for 12 to 14 days. Because of this limited shelf life, many a New England trawler returns to port with some fish of marginal quality and with a catch equal to only about 30 percent of its maximum carrying capacity.

Most of the fish caught in New England waters are filleted in processing plants located in ports in Massachusetts and Maine, and then sold. Although there is an increasing demand for fresh fish by restaurants and supermarkets, most of the catch must be sold in the frozen state because of the very limited keeping quality of fish stored in ice. Only the last-caught fish landed by the fishing trawlers, which may be 5 to 6 days old, are of good enough quality to be sold as fresh fillets.

It can be seen that there is a definite need to increase the keeping quality of fish while they are still on the vessel. Considerable research has been conducted on the freezing of fish at sea, but the industry is reluctant to adopt this solution. Fish processed in this way would cost more, largely because of the high initial cost of the required facilities. Moreover, it is doubted that the increased price of processing could be recovered on the highly competitive frozen food market, where prices are strongly influenced by imports from Canada, Iceland, and other countries.

What is obviously needed is a method of keeping fish in their natural fresh state for a longer time. Such a development would:
1. Enable vessels to stay at sea a longer time and return home with a full hold of saleable product.
2. Enable vessels to land more fish of higher quality which could be sold at premium prices now commanded by fresh fish.
3. Make it possible for non-frozen fish to be sold in quantity in the densely populated interior of the country, thus benefitting both the fishing industry and the long denied inland consumers.
4. Make it possible to stabilize supply and demand for fish, with benefits to producers, processors, distributors, and purchasers alike.
5. Contribute to conservation of fish supply by making it more feasible to fish waters further from shore.

Radiation pasteurization may well provide the answer. The USAEC is

Typical trawlers used by American fishermen out of Gloucester, Massachusetts. Most of these ships are over 25 years old.

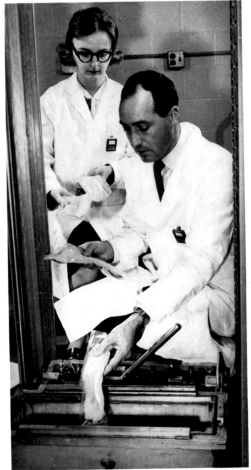

Prepackaged fish being placed in irradiation chamber at the Massachusetts Institute of Technology's Food Technology Laboratory. Chamber is lowered into a water pit containing 30,000 curies of cobalt 60.

After irradiation and a period of storage the fish are cooked and evaluated by a taste panel.

sponsoring research in this field at several Bureau of Commercial Fisheries laboratories and at a number of universities. Scientists carrying out these investigations feel that irradiating fish as soon as they are landed on the vessel will delay the growth of bacteria, the principal reason for adverse quality changes in ground fish, and thus result in a substantial extension of shelf life. Indications are, for example, that the shelf life of refrigerated haddock can be extended to 30 days if it is irradiated when only one day old. If, however, irradiation is delayed until the fish is seven days old, the extension of life would be for only eleven additional days.

The next stage in the development of the technology will be the completion of the USAEC's Marine Products Development Irradiator at Gloucester, Massachusetts, scheduled for late summer 1964. This unit will have a capacity for handling a ton of fish each hour by means of a cobalt 60 source of approximately 250,000 curies. It should provide important data on the practicality and economics of the process.

Preservation of Fruit.

Another USAEC-sponsored program involves the radiation preservation of fruit. A basic problem is the presence of rot organisms which manifest themselves while the products are in distribution channels, resulting in a serious curtailment of quality and market life. Equally important is the fact that certain fruits, such as cherries and various types of berries, have naturally short physiological lives. As a consequence, extensive culling of spoiled fruit is frequently required at the receiving markets, and some product is lost totally when it is considered too perishable for shipment. Experiments, mainly at the Davis campus of the University of California, have demonstrated that radiation can reduce considerably the amount of such losses.

The most favorable results obtained to date appear to be those with strawberries. A dose of 200 kilorads gives a significant retardation of decay, with no severe adverse effects on quality. The research at Davis indicates that certain other fruits also respond well to radiation doses varying from 150 KR to 400 KR as far as resistance to decay is concerned, but with

Comparison of irradiated and non-irradiated strawberries after 8 days of storage at 41°F.

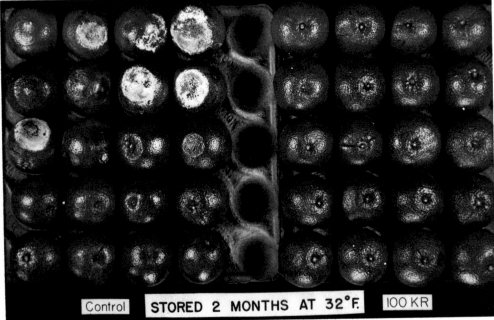

Comparison of irradiated and non-irradiated oranges after 2 months of storage at 32°F.

varying effects on quality. Thus, cherries retain their ascorbic acid content but suffer some loss in crispness of the flesh. Raspberries also tend to soften, although their flavor is not adversely affected. Nectarines retain flavor and resistance to mechanical injury, but suffer a marked loss of texture. Washington navel oranges withstand the treatment well, but with some adverse effect on taste.

Losses of quality of the types noted above might in several cases not be so great as to preclude commercial acceptance. In such cases the adoption of radiation preservation by industry might turn importantly on economic factors.

The potential economic benefits can be summarized as follows:
1. By reducing the proportion of the crop which succumbs to decay, the total amount marketed would be increased, especially the amount marketed as fresh fruit.
2. The present practice of shipping fruit before it is mature to curtail losses could be discontinued to a large extent. The result would be the marketing of fruit of higher quality which might command higher prices.
3. More distant markets could be opened up to short-lived produce, thus increasing the total amounts sold.

Against these benefits it would of course be necessary to balance the incremental costs occasioned by irradiation.

More information is expected to be obtained, and the technology further advanced, through large-scale studies of fruit processing, particularly on the West coast. A mobile cobalt 60 irradiator is being designed for this purpose.

Radiation preservation of food probably still has considerable development to undergo before the technique is used commercially in the United States. Assurance that this is a safe and acceptable method is the preliminary, but very important first step. When clearance has been obtained for a sufficient number of commercially interesting foods, economics and public acceptance will probably determine whether or not this technique will come into widespread usage.

Sterilization of Surgical Sutures

For many years the standard means for sterilizing surgical sutures was through sustained heat application in a high-boiling hydrocarbon mixture named Cumol. This method requires awkward handling procedures during manufacture. Each suture is sterilized while in an open tube. After sterilization the container is filled with a sterile tubing fluid and sealed. To minimize the danger of recontamination, these post-sterilization operations must be carried out under aseptic conditions equivalent to those in operating rooms, workers being required to scrub and to wear gowns and gloves.

Because of these handling requirements, suture sterilization by heat has been a batch process. Hence, the manufacturing economies obtainable from automation and the continuous flow of materials have not been available. A further problem is a very narrow safety margin. The lethal heat dose of the most resistant microorganisms has been found to be about $300°F$; cumolization is accomplished at $314°F$, a margin of only 5 percent. The application of heat also deprives the sutures of tensile strength, and, in the case of the absorbable type of suture known as catgut (about 60 to 70 percent of all sutures are of this type), it causes a loss of pliability. A final dissatisfaction with heat sterilization is that experienced in the operating room where it is necessary to break a glass tube in order to extricate each suture.

It was with these difficulties in mind that Ethicon, Inc., a division of Johnson & Johnson, began in 1949 to investigate the possibility of utilizing radiation instead of heat as the means of sterilization.

Early in 1953 Ethicon acquired a 2-Mev Van de Graaff accelerator for its Somerville, New Jersey, plant. The research conducted with this machine demonstrated that electron beam sterilization of sutures was entirely feasible, except in the case of cotton sutures (about 5 percent of total production) which are degraded by radiation sterilization doses. It was found, however, that an energy of at least 5 Mev was needed to penetrate the largest items in Ethicon's line; also that higher power than the Van de Graaff's 500 watts was needed.

Late in 1957, therefore, Ethicon began installation of a 6 Mev Microwave Linear Accelerator with a maximum power output of 4.2 kilowatts; specifications sufficient for large-scale commercial sterilization. By April 1958 the company had converted the bulk of its sterilization operations to the new process. Later, a second linear accelerator, rated at 7 Mev, was added to take care of increased production requirements.

The results have been highly satisfactory. One of the chief benefits has been the introduction of continuous, automated processing, which is more economical than the batch processing necessitated by the previous aseptic packaging, and which makes possible reductions in packaging, handling and shipping costs.

Ethicon has also been able to market the radiation-sterilized suture as essentially a new and superior product. As contrasted to the 10 to 20 percent loss in tensile strength caused by heat sterilization, electron beam sterilization, causes a loss of only 4 to 8 percent. This means that surgeons can now safely use smaller sutures than previously. Further, radiation-sterilized catgut sutures are more pliable than those sterilized by heat.

In addition, the safety margin is now much greater. The sterilizing dose of 2.5 megarads exceeds the lethal dose for the most resistant microorganisms by 40%, as opposed to the narrow 5% margin previously obtained. Moreover, because sterilization now takes place after packaging, all danger of recontamination is eliminated.

Perhaps the greatest improvement made is in packaging. An aluminium foil package has been adopted which is impermeable, attractive, shaped for efficient stacking, and easy to open by tearing. Sterilization takes place after the suture is sealed in the package.

Other suture manufacturers have now begun to introduce radiation sterilization. It is estimated that more than two-thirds of the sutures produced in the United Statees are radiation-sterilized. A variety of other medical supplies, including syringes, gloves, and surgical dressings, are also being irradiated.

Ethicon is now building a plant in San Angelo, Texas, where it will sterilize sutures with a cobalt 60 source rather than

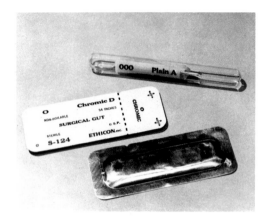

Comparison of Cumol sterilized suture in vial with electron sterilized suture package.

View of Ethicon Inc., plant at Sommerville, New Jersey showing employees packaging sutures prior to irradiation.

Tray which holds suture packages during irradiation process.

with accelerators. The new plant will be completed in the latter half of 1964, and will initially contain 60,000 curies of cobalt 60.

According to Dr. Charles Artandi, Associate Director of Research, and one of the pioneers in the development of Ethicon's radiation processes, the primary reasons for this change are the expectations of lower maintenance and operating costs and less down time (the cobalt 60 unit requires fewer people and they need not be so highly trained). Furthermore, whereas the accelerator must treat suture packages one by one, the greater penetrating power of the cobalt 60 unit's gamma rays will make it possible to irradiate stacks of sutures at one time. The dose rates from cobalt 60 are lower than those from the accelerators, so that exposure times will have to be longer in order to achieve sterility. This can be accepted, however, in view of the fact that the cobalt 60 unit will be emitting energy around the clock. Moreover, according to Dr. Artandi, replacement of cobalt 60 can be scheduled so that maximum capacity will be available at times of peak treatment loads.

All of these advantages of cobalt 60 have been demonstrated by the operation of two associated plants in England. One is the Johnson Ethical Products, Ltd. plant at Slough, England, where hypodermic syringes have been sterilized with cobalt 60 irradiation since 1962; the other is the Ethicon, Ltd. plant at Edinburgh, Scotland, which became operational early in 1963.

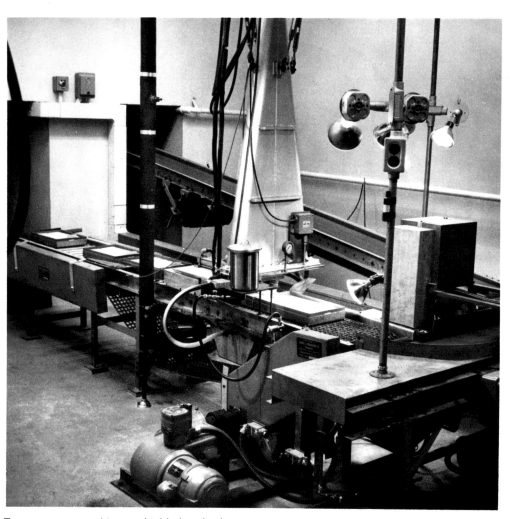

Trays are conveyed into a shielded vault where they are exposed to 6 Mev electrons from a linear accelerator.

Chapter 6
Synthesis of Chemicals

Synthesis of Chemicals

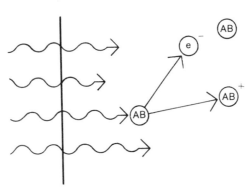

It has been established for many years that high energy radiation can initiate chemical reactions. Although this subject has been the focus of many research investigations rather little has been learned of the exact mechanisms involved. It seems clear that it is a very complicated process. In a very simplified way radiation chemists picture the process as starting with ionization. That is, as the incoming radiation interacts with a molecule, an electron detaches itself from the molecule of which it was a part, leaving a positively charged ion. In some cases the electron flies off with enough energy to cause further ionization. In other cases, it attaches itself to a neutral molecule to form a negatively charged ion.

The positively charged ion will quickly have its charge neutralized by a stray electron in its vicinity and will turn into a highly agitated or excited molecule. The excited molecule in turn can break up into two or more free radicals, that is, highly reactive forms of molecules containing a pair of electrons in such positions that they can be held jointly by two atoms. Sometimes the excited molecule will form directly by interaction with the incoming radiation. The positive ion can also interact chemically with neutral molecules and stray electrons to form new chemical molecules. The free radicals can recombine to form the original molecule or can interact with themselves or other molecules in their vicinity to form new chemical molecules. The negatively charged ions can undergo chemical reactions similar to those of the positively charged ions.

As to the time scale of these events, it is very likely that in the first attosecond (10^{-18} sec) molecules in the track of the incoming radiation are ionized and other molecules electronically excited. Probably in the next picosecond (10^{-12} sec)

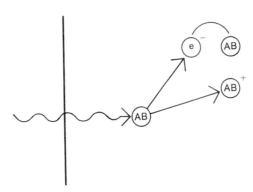

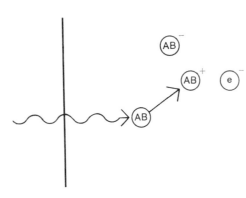

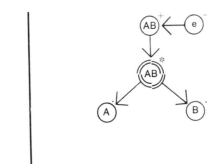

various excited molecules break apart into free radicals. Between the first picosecond and a microsecond (10^{-6} sec) there is probably a competition between radical combination and radical diffusion which is affected by the nature of the incident radiation and the physical state of the matter thru which the radiation is passing.

If the interacting radiation is a gamma ray or high energy electron travelling through matter the loss of energy per unit length of path is relatively low. Clusters of reactive molecules are sufficiently far apart so that some radicals diffuse out of the cluster and react in the surrounding medium. If the incident radiation is a heavy particle such as an alpha particle or fission fragment the energy loss per unit length of path is very high; the clusters of reactive molecules coalesce and the reactions occur mainly within the path.

If the medium through which the radiation is passing is a gas the ions and their descendants have a better chance to diffuse away from the cluster than if the medium is liquid.

The fact that these chemical reactions take place in tracks and clusters rather than homogeneously throughout the medium make the nature of the reaction products and their yields difficult to predict by general principles so that one must depend upon empirical information to postulate an effect.

While not knowing how radiation-induced reactions occur, industrial chemists have still been able to determine by empirical investigation the reaction products which can be produced by irradiating various substances, and also the rate and amount of this production. Before radiation is adopted for any specific use, however, it must demonstrate some net advantage over thermal or catalytic means of inducing chemical reactions.

Radiation does appear to have certain unique capabilities. For example, since radiation fields are controllable, it is possible by means of radiation to deposit ions, free radicals, or other excited species which can initiate chemical reactions in desired space and time configurations. Furthermore, in theory at least, one can obtain with radiation a planned non-uniform distribution of radicals, if that is desired. It is difficult to achieve such

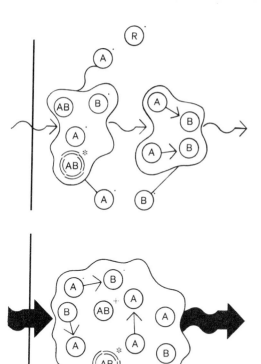

control with chemically formed free radicals. Another advantage of radiation techniques is that they initiate reactions without adding chemical contaminants.

A limiting factor is the matter of cost. At present electron accelerators and isotopes are relatively expensive sources of process energy and generally cannot compete economically with conventional energy sources in large volume chemical processes. There are several examples, however, of processes that have been commercially developed. Some of these processes are discussed in the following pages. As the cost of large-scale production radiation sources drops, and improved technology increases reaction efficiency, it is anticipated that the number of commercial applications will grow.

Manufacture of Ethyl Bromide

The knowledge that high energy radiation can initiate chemical reactions is approximately 50 years old. Little serious consideration was given to practical applications of this phenomenon, however, until about 1951 when cobalt 60 was made commercially available in cylinders suitable for use in research.

In the next several years many industrial organizations acquired cobalt 60 facilities, and research on possible commercial applications proceeded apace. There was, nevertheless, a further delay until 1963 before an actual commercial process based on radiation was introduced.

The delay appears to have been caused principally by the fact that radiation-based processes which were proven technically feasible in the laboratory appeared to be too costly in relation to alternative methods. This cost factor was probably reinforced by a resistance to getting involved with safety problems and other novel aspects of radiation in the absence of unmistakable commercial advantage. Against this background it is interesting to review how the first commercial utilization came about. It involved the introduction of a radiation process by the Dow Chemical Company for manufacture of ethyl bromide.

Ethyl bromide is a volatile organic liquid whose chief role at present is as an intermediate for organic synthesis. Dow has been manufacturing this product for many years, utilizing a reaction between hydrogen bromide and ethyl alcohol. Difficulties with this system which led to the search for a better one are best described in the words of Dr. David E. Harmer, who developed the radiation process:

"One problem we had with the old system was that a large part of the ethyl alcohol was eliminated as water during reaction with hydrogen bromide. This made it necessary for us to discard one-third the weight of the alcohol. The by-product water also carried with it substantial amounts of hydrogen bromide. A process which would replace ethyl alcohol with ethylene would eliminate this loss."

A process based on radiation was only one of several alternative ways of making this change. The reasoning which prompted its adoption in preference to the alternatives is further described by Dr. Harmer: "It was known that the desired reaction between ethylene and hydrogen bromide could be initiated by free radicals which, in turn, could be produced alternatively by chemical catalyst systems, ultraviolet light, or high energy radiation.

"The chemical catalyst one would normally consider for such a reaction is some form of peroxide. But peroxide is both costly and dangerous to handle. The other practical possibility among chemical catalysts appeared to be aluminum halide. It was unattractive for two reasons: (1) it must be replaced from time to time or suitably recycled, either of which processes would be costly; (2) it is easily destroyed by moisture entering the system.

"Both ultraviolet light and high energy radiation are clean catalytic agents. But the U-V system was rather quickly eliminated because its costs, both for operation and maintenance, appeared high when compared with those of high energy radiation for the particular conditions involved in this reaction.

"As far as high energy radiation was concerned, electron beam energy was not seriously considered since most free radical reactions become decreasingly efficient at high dose rates, and localized dose rates would be very high with electron beams. Thus, by a process of elimination we came to gamma radiation as the best system available. It was best because it was free of technical problems which beset other system and because it was the least costly."

A factor in the favorable economics of the radiation process was that it required only 1800 curies of cobalt 60. This involved a replacement cost for cobalt 60 of only $300 per year, and required no costly complications in plant design.

The radiation process ultimately developed involves the recirculation of liquid ethyl bromide through an external heat exchanger and then through an underground reaction vessel. Feed streams of gaseous ethylene and hydrogen bromide are added to the recycled ethyl bromide stream and react as they pass through the irradiated zone. The new product formed from this reaction overflows from the surge tank into a

Shell of reaction vessel for ethyl bromide production being lowered into position at Dow Chemical Company's Midland, Michigan plant.

distillation apparatus where purification of the product begins. Purification is completed by the neutralization of small amounts of unreacted hydrogen bromide in a sodium hydroxide scrubber followed by drying and storage. The product is shipped either in drums or tank cars.

The radiation-based production facility has an annual production capability of about 1,000,000 pounds of ethyl bromide. It has replaced entirely the older unit which employed the ethyl alcohol process.

The actual start-up of the plant in 1963 was not without its trying moments. In order to be able to employ the recirculating system from the very start, the reaction vessel and surge tank were filled with ethyl bromide made previously by the ethyl alcohol process. It was known from laboratory experience that a significant induction period could be expected as a result of various free radical inhibitors found in ethyl bromide made in this manner. It was also known that iron contamination from new equipment would cause a similar induction period until the new system had operated long enough to be completely cleaned.

The operators cleaned the ethyl bromide as best they could, started the circulation, began adding ethylene and hydrogen bromide, and waited for the reaction between these two materials to start. Four suspenseful days passed without any sign of the reaction. During the fifth day a reaction became apparent, but at very slow rates. It was not until the ninth day that desired reaction rates were reached. They have been maintained ever since.

Cobalt source in lead container being lowered into position in reaction vessel.

Entire facility for radiation production of ethyl bromide consists of one underground reaction vessel. Public is permitted to view cover of the facility while it is in operation.

A New Packaging Material

A polymer is a compound of high molecular weight formed by joining together two or more single molecules or radicals. One classification of polymers divides them into amorphous and crystalline structures. In the amorphous state the molecules are distributed and oriented in a random fashion and are usually coiled if they are not too stiff. In this state molecules can show considerable thermal motion, likened to that of writhing snakes. Crystalline structures are those in which the molecules, or at least long segments of them, are precisely aligned, precisely positioned, and precisely oriented relative to each other. It frequently occurs as, for example, in commercial polyethylene, that crystalline and amorphous structures are interspersed.

When a polymer such as polyethylene is irradiated at ambient temperature, an active radical is produced in each of two molecules in the amorphous region. The molecules writhe toward each other and react. When this occurs, a link is formed between the two. This process is called crosslinking.

The W. R. Grace Co. took advantage of this phenomenon to produce a new polyethylene packaging film called CRYOVAC. The company also gave the name CRYOVAC to its patented process for vacuumizing, sealing, and shrinking the packaging film around refrigerated foods in the form of an airtight bag. The shrink characteristic is built into the film by stretching it in two directions in the course of manufacture. This orients the film biaxially. The product is then enclosed in a plastic bag and vacuumized. After this the film can be shrunk by the application of heat to fit any shape or size of product.

W. L. Grace's first packaging films based on CRYOVAC processes were made of polyvinylidene chloride. This is a material which possesses heat shrinkable properties and is relatively impermeable to the transfer of moisture or oxygen, i.e., it is "non-breathing." It was commercially successful for quite a number of years as a wrapper for perishable meat and poultry products. But relatively few products either require or can afford the luxury of a dense non-breathing film

Start of the trip to the electron beam generator at the Cryovac Division of W. R. Grace & Co., Duncan, South Carolina. Extruded polyethylene tape feeds into a vault extending 30 feet below ground.

Polyethylene tape being irradiated as it passes under window of 2-mev electron beam generator. The tape is next biaxially stretched into film and wound into rolls.

Top portion of underground vault. The dome of the accelerator is seen in foreground. The polyethylene tape feeding into the lower portion is shown toward the rear of vault.

Completed polyethylene film being inspected
for quality control.

like polyvinylidene chloride. In fact, many of the products which constitute the biggest potential packaging markets, e.g., produce, baked goods, and fresh meat, require packages that breathe. Thus, company officials came to the conclusion that there would be a great potential for a breathing film that could also shrink, particularly if it were (1) strong enough to stand consumer abuse at all temperatures, (2) readily adaptable to high speed automatic machine application, (3) endowed with good clarity and gloss, and (4) competitive in cost.

Attention quickly focussed on polyethylene, which was found to have some of the desired characteristics. However, unlike polyvinylidene chloride, polyethylene was too weak in its basic molecular structure to withstand biaxial orientation without breaking.

After attempts to strengthen the molecular structure of polyethylene by various other methods proved unsuccessful, it was decided to use radiation to supply just enough crosslinking to hold the polyethylene molecules together. The result was a polyethylene material that possesses all of the required characteristics. It is strong enough to orient easily and without breakage, it is as clear and glossy as cellophane, is six to eight times as strong as conventional polyethylene, and is sufficiently heat-resistant to be successfully heat-sealed over a wide range of temperatures. Above all, the film has exceptional shrinking characteristics—it shrinks rapidly and remains in its new shape with a high degree of shrink tension. Finally, the material sells in a price range competitive with that of cellophane and conventional polyethylene.

The commercial process involves, first, the extrusion of low density polyethylene into a heavy tape. The tape is then passed under a 2-mev beam generator for crosslinking. After irradiation the material is slit slightly and then stretched in both directions more than 100%. It is then cooled and set in its new direction. The resultant film is wound into rolls which may be printed, slit, and sized for individual customers and applications.

The CRYOVAC Division's several generators can turn out more than two million pounds of film per year, and the company plans to install additional

An application of irradiated polyethylene film. It provides an attractive, economical, and sanitary wrapper for these pears.

production capacity as new markets develop.

This process illustrates one of the unique advantages of high energy radiation—it is able to modify a finished product. It also provides a good illustration of a set of processing conditions which can utilize electron beams advantageously relative to other sources of radiation. The conditions involved in this case are that the penetration required is low, and that the reaction dose is independent of the intensity of radiation applied.

Developing a Foamless Detergent

As the uses of synthetic detergents have risen, they have sometimes left behind, along with their numerous benefits to housewives and others, a residue of foam on streams and in public water supplies. There have been isolated instances where foaming on streams has been so great as to interfere with navigation. On other occasions, foam has appeared in household tap water.

There does not appear to be any established evidence that the foam endangers health, but the phenomenon has nevertheless aroused considerable public concern all over the world. As a consequence, the use of certain existing types of detergents has been forbidden by law in West Germany, in the State of Wisconsin, and in one county in Florida. Similar legislation is being considered in the United States Congress and elsewhere.

How has this problem arisen? The basic trouble has been that bacteria, which readily devour waste soap products when they enter sewage streams, have shown a disinclination to digest certain synthetic detergents, i.e., in their present form these detergents are not sufficiently "biodegradable."

The culprit which has caused the foaming problem is a hydrocarbon derivative called alkybenzene sulfonate—ABS for short—introduced shortly after World War II. More than one billion pounds of it a year are used for detergent manufacture in the United States and Europe.

By January 1966, not one pound of ABS is expected to be used in the manufacture of household detergents in the United States. The soap companies which market detergents, and the petroleum and chemical companies which supply them, are in the midst of a vigorous program to find and produce one or more satisfactory biodegradable detergents. Detergent producers are competing vigorously for shares in the large market and a variety of new biodegradable detergents has been or is being developed.

ABS is non-biodegradable for reasons having to do with its molecular structure, which is "branched", that is, its molecules are composed of groupings of atoms which stick out at angles. The new bio-

degradable detergents being developed all have a linear hydrocarbon structure which bacteria seem to find more palatable. The new products will utilize straight chain paraffins, olefins or alcohols as the basic raw materials.

A uniquely different approach has been adopted by scientists at the Esso Research and Engineering Company, an affiliate of Standard Oil Company of New Jersey. They have employed gamma rays from a cobalt-60 facility at Esso's Linden, New Jersey, research center, to achieve synthesis of a good surfactant molecule based on the sodium salt of an alkane sulfonic acid (SAS). This chemical compound is comprised of sulfonate groups randomly distributed along an essentially straight hydrocarbon chain. The critical steps employed in the reaction were first investigated by an Esso chemist, Dr. James F. Black, after years of research on applications of nuclear radiations.

Various methods of bringing about the desired reaction were considered by the Esso scientists and engineers. Electron beam equipment was found to be more costly than cobalt 60 for this purpose and to present a heat build-up problem. The poor penetrating power of beta emitters was found to present serious design problems. X-ray equipment was considered too cumbersome and expensive. Ultra-violet light is chemically inefficient for this reaction, and since highly absorptive solutions are not uncommon, its poor penetrating power causes reactor design problems similar to those encountered with beta emitters. Chemical activation appeared unsuitable because of problems associated with impurities likely to be found in the feedstock and residues left in the product. By contrast, cobalt 60 is relatively low in cost, presents no heat build-up problem, and has great penetrating power which allows for freedom and flexibility in designing reactor pressure vessels and internals. Moreover, the cobalt 60 radiation does not in any way make the product radioactive.

At this writing (May 1964), study of SAS's suitability as a surfactant has reached a semi-commercial scale, with work on a laboratory and pilot plant basis essentially complete. There seems to be

little doubt that suitable detergent formulations of SAS can be found for a wide variety of household and commercial applications. What remains to be determined is how Esso's product will compare in suitability to those being developed by other manufacturers using other methods.

It is evident that three criteria will be employed by the soap and detergent manufacturers in determining which of the new detergents they will adopt. These are: (1) biodegradability; (2) efficiency as a cleanser; and (3) cost.

On the first point, SAS has been investigated in the laboratory, and in pilot plant and full-scale sewage plant demonstrations. These tests show it to be more rapidly and completely biodegradable than the best linear alkylbenzene sulfonates. The laboratory and pilot plant test further show SAS to be about as biodegradable as fatty alcohol sulfates (the most biodegradable surfactants known); in fact, to be in this respect roughly equivalent to soap.

Esso spokesmen further state that SAS has shown itself to be equivalent to ABS as a cleanser of textiles, the single most important detergent application. Work is still under way to select formulations which will give the complete range of foaming abilities desired in today's diverse detergent applications.

Perhaps the principal unanswered question concerns the relative economic merits of the competing products when all factors such as detergency, biodegradability and various quality characteristics are considered. While definitive results are not yet available, Esso officials are optimistic that the company's product will hold up well in this respect.

As of May 1964 detailed plans for a plant to produce SAS were being prepared. If such a plant is built it would mark a significant step forward in the development of radiation chemistry technology in that the amount of cobalt 60 required would be considerably greater than that used in the Dow ethyl bromide plant discussed earlier.

Interior of hot cell at Esso Research Center, Linden, New Jersey, showing reaction vessels in which cobalt 60 is used to synthesize bio-degradable detergents on a pilot plant scale.

Engineering equipment used prior and subsequent to cobalt 60 initiation of primary reaction in the experimental production of biodegradable detergents at the Esso Research Center.

Future Trends in Radiation Chemistry

As can be seen from the preceding examples, some commercialization of radiation chemistry has taken place. Research and development leading to further applications is steadily increasing. One interesting area of research is the study of the polymerization of ethylene being undertaken at Brookhaven National Laboratory. Within the range of process conditions investigated it appears that polyethylene of a good commercial quality could be synthesized competitively by a radiation process. Although this work requires elaboration on a larger scale to validate the present tentative conclusions, it justifies hope of a very large scale application.

An even more interesting development is the Brookhaven work on radiation-produced copolymers of ethylene. It has been shown possible to copolymerize ethylene with each of twenty different monomers, ranging from unsaturated hydrocarbons, through halogenated hydrocarbons, to the acrylates, acetates, acrylonitrile, sulphur dioxide, and carbon monoxide.

The copolymer of ethylene and carbon monoxide may have particular promise for commercial application. Data in the literature indicate that with conventional thermal-catalytic methods it can be produced only in waxes of low molecular weight. The reason for this is believed to be that a reversible reaction occurs during the chain propagating step because of the higher temperatures needed to produce the radical from the internal catalysts required for initiating the polymerization. By contrast, it has been found that the radiation-produced polymer made at temperatures of 25°-50°C is a polyketone of high molecular weight and that it can be formed into a tough plastic film. The radiation-produced polymer has been shown further to have concentrations of carbon monoxide in the range of 25% to 50%, thus substantially decreasing costs for raw materials.

Other areas in radiation chemistry being investigated in the United States include not only further chemical chain reactions such as polymerizations, but also endothermic reactions such as the fixation of nitrogen, the synthesis of hydrazine and the synthesis of ozone where nuclear reactors rather than radioisotope sources would provide the energy input to the system.

One concludes that this is an exciting field to study, and one whose commercial potential has yet to be fully explored.

Chapter 7
Other Isotope Applications
in Industry

Other Isotope Applications in Industry

A sheet of plastic (right) passing through a radioisotope device which both measures and controls its thickness.

In Chapters 5 and 6 we considered the industrial use of isotope sources for sterilization and to initiate chemical reactions. These are relatively new applications which have great future potential but which are not now widely employed. This chapter is devoted to the great bulk of what are now virtually routine uses of radioisotopes in industry. These are now so widespread and various that we cannot in the space available cover more than a small fraction. Consequently, we have considered it best to confine ourselves to a discussion of some of the more important procedures with which radioisotopes are currently employed in industry, followed by a brief discussion of some of the specific applications found in a single industry. We have chosen the petroleum industry for this purpose because it is probably the single industry which uses radioisotopes most extensively.

Isotopes are used routinely in industry in three main ways—for gaging, radiography, and tracer studies. In addition, there has been some development of uses involving activation analysis, static dissipation, and luminescence.

Gaging

Gaging applications have to date been
by far the most numerous. The principle
involved is that material placed between a
source of radiation and a detector will
scatter or absorb some of the radiation.
The extent to which this occurs will
give information about the material's
position, density, or thickness.

Advantages of using radioisotopes
rather than conventional methods
for gaging are: (1) no mechanical contact
is made with the gaged material—this
is often important where the material is
corrosive, toxic, or otherwise dangerous or
difficult to handle; (2) the measurements
can be made continuously at remote
locations; and (3) the gaging signals can
in many cases be fed to automatic
devices so that not only information about,
but actual control over, thickness,
density, position, etc., can be obtained.

Gaging the Level of Liquids

Various methods are available whereby
radioactive sources can be used to
measure the level of a liquid within a
closed container. Perhaps the simplest is
to have a radioactive source floating on
top of the liquid. A detector is then
moved up and down outside the container
until its maximum reading shows the
level of the source.

Where conditions do not favor having
a source inside the container, the source
and detector can be mounted on
opposite sides of the container and moved
up or down simultaneously. An abrupt
increase in radiation will indicate that the
rays are no longer passing through the
liquid and that the surface level
has been passed.

A more complicated device involves
a servo-mechanism controlled by the
strength of the radiations which move the
source and detector up and down the
tank at the same level as the liquid.

Gamma sources are generally required
for level indicators because the radiations
must have sufficient energy to penetrate
the walls of a containing vessel.

Thickness Gaging

There are two main methods for using
isotopes to measure and control thickness.
The first and most common involves

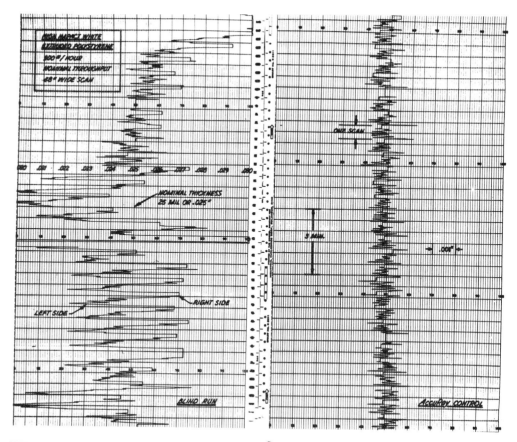

Some results obtained with a radioisotope
thickness-control device. On left one can see
the wide variations in thickness of plastic sheet
which resulted from production without the
device; and on right the much greater uniformity achieved with the device.

A gamma backscatter gauge being used for
density control in a road paving project. The
gauge makes a density measurement of hot
(300°F) asphaltic concrete immediately after
it is poured and between successive roller
passes. Rolling patterns can then be quickly
set up and verified, optimum rolling temperatures determined, and the comparative effect
of various types of rollers evaluated.

feeding a sheet of material between a radioactive source and a detector. Variations in thickness will affect the intensity of radiation reaching the detector. The intensity of radiation which should come through the desired thickness having been determined, any variations from this amount can be made to trigger an electric signal which adjusts operational machinery to bring thickness back to specifications.

Sometimes a situation arises where it is possible to approach only one side of a material. Or it may be desired to gage the thickness of a coating material placed on a backing of another material. In these instances both the source and detector are placed on the same side of the material. What is measured is the intensity of radiation reflected or "backscattered", which increases in proportion to the thickness of the material being measured until a saturation value is reached.

In thickness gaging, beta ray sources are utilized for thinner materials like paper, plastics, and rubber tire fabrics. Gamma radiation is needed for heavier material such as metal sheet up to several inches in thickness or tubing of large diameter.

Density Gaging

The method employed in density gaging is basically similar to the "transmission" method of thickness gaging, with source and detector placed on opposite sides of the material. Thickness of the material measured is held constant so that differences in radiation intensity can be ascribed to variations in density only.

Radioisotope density gauges provide means for continuous measurement of density, specific gravity, per cent solids, concentration, or related quantity of materials conveyed in pipes. Using an encapsulated radioisotope as a source of radiation, the system analyzes composition of materials from the exterior of the pipe without contacting the measured material; a distinct advantage when dealing with corrosive, erosive, abrasive, viscous, or high pressure fluids. Here we see a device (bottom) being used to control the per cent of solids in a coal slurry.

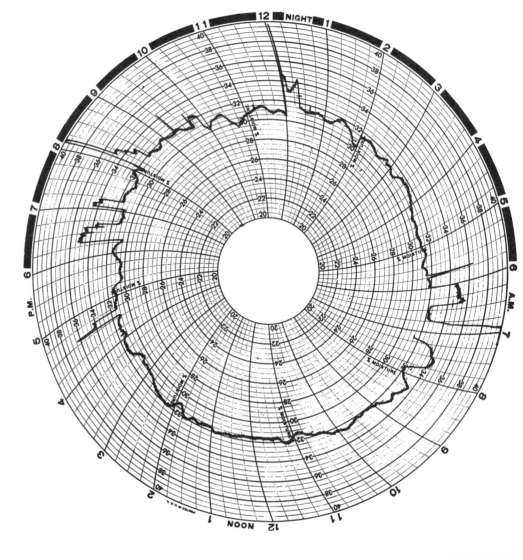

A radioisotope density gauge being used to test soil compaction on a highway construction project.

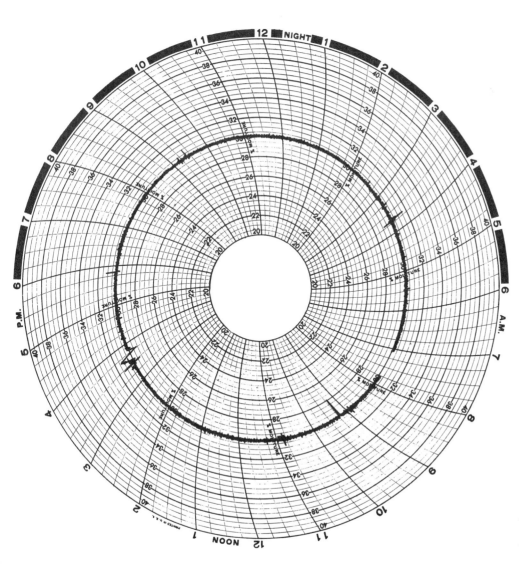

Graphs showing improvement obtained by use of a radioisotope density-control device in controlling kiln feed in a typical cement processing plant. The graph at left shows that there were wide variations in moisture content when the device was not employed. The graph at right shows the far greater uniformity obtained with the device.

Radiography

Radiography, like gaging, is made possible by the ability of radiation to penetrate matter. The need frequently arises in industry to inspect castings, welds and other products of heavy engineering by photographing their interiors. A piece of photographic film is placed against the test object, which is located between the radiation source and the film. Any crack or break in the object will increase the amount of radiation which strikes the film so that sections of the film, when developed, will appear darker than the remainder.

Both X ray and radioisotope sources can be used for this procedure. Radioisotope sources are being increasingly favored because they are less expensive, because their small size makes it possible to radiograph places where an X-ray machine would not fit, and because no power source is required. It is well to recognize certain relative advantages of X rays. X ray devices are faster because of the high intensities available; the energy can be adjusted (whereas each isotope has a fixed energy); and there is no problem of decay.

A variant of radiography is autoradiography. Radioactive material spread over a smooth surface can usually make a record of its own distribution if X-ray film is placed in intimate contact with the surface. The radioactive spots expose the emulsion of the film. This technique has proven useful in detecting imperfections in paint coatings because radioactive gas directed against the coating will reveal only those spots where imperfections exist.

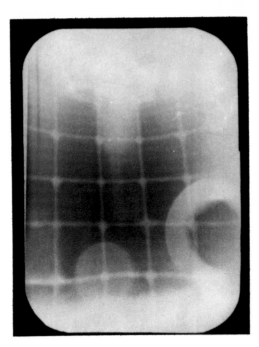

Radiograph of automobile engine block section containing no flaws.

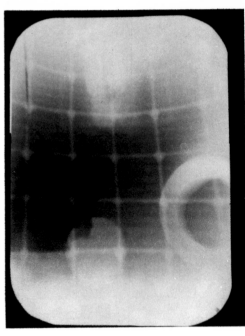

Radiograph of engine block section containing a void in the aluminum wall behind the cylinder liner. The dark, triangular-shaped area is evidence of the void.

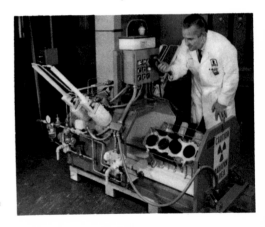

Radiography unit being used to inspect an automobile engine block.

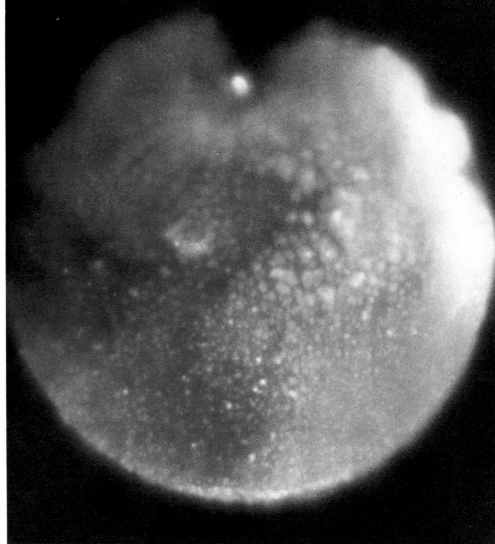

First picture shows ordinary photograph of engine deposits on a cylinder head. Second picture is an autoradiograph of the same deposits, indicating the distribution (lighter spots and areas) of a gasoline ignition control additive which had been labeled with phosphorus 32. The autoradiograph gave valuable information on the behavior of the additive to its manufacturer.

32568

Tracer Applications

A large number of ingenious applications have been found in industry for radioactive tracers. Many of these are based on the extraordinary sensitivity of tracer techniques, i.e., the fact that they make it possible to detect exceedingly minute amounts of material, estimated to be as small as a billion billionth (10^{-18}) of an ounce. Another attribute most useful in industry is the ability to detect tracers through solid walls.

Leak Detection

Isotope tracers offer a simple, sure, and inexpensive method of detecting leaks in pipes carrying liquids such as water or petroleum. A small amount of radioactivity is added to the flow. Any liquid which leaks out can then usually be located, even if concealed from view.

Wear Measurement

Wear can be measured with great sensitivity by tracer techniques. The method is described below in the discussion of petroleum industry applications.

Flow Measurement

Radioisotope tracers provide simple and accurate means for measuring the flow rate of liquids and gases without interfering with the flow. The detecting devices can sometimes be coupled with electric signals which, fed back to control valves and pumps, automatically regulate the flow rate.

A method commonly used is to add a known quantity of tracer material to the stream. Calculations based on measurement of total radioactivity at a point below the place of introduction will then reveal the speed of flow.

Alternatively, neutrons may be shot through a liquid-carrying pipe by an accelerator. The small amount of radioactivity induced is detected by a radiation counter a short way downstream. The amount of radiation is directly proportional to the flow rate since the slower the flow rate the greater the amount of radioactivity which will decay.

Mixing Tests

By using radioisotopes various measurements which depend on mixing ratios can be made quickly and accurately. One method involves the so-called isotope dilution technique, commonly used by physicians to measure blood or water volume in the human body. To determine the quantity of a substance in a mixture, a small, known quantity of a radioisotope of the substance is added. Then an amount of the substance is separated from the mixture and the proportion of radioactivity to weight calculated. A simple arithmetic ratio reveals the quantity of the substance in the mixture.

Often in industry there is need to assure that an additive is thoroughly mixed with some bulk material. If the additive can be made to contain a radioisotope, then its distribution can be checked by measuring radioactiivty in equal samples drawn at random from the bulk material.

Miscellaneous Techniques

Activation Analysis

The relatively new technique of activation analysis is coming into use in industry for detecting and estimating small traces of elements. For example, the presence of exceedingly small impurities can severely injure the quality of silicon. By activation analysis it is possible to discern traces of arsenic and copper in silicon as small as one part in ten thousand million.

As discussed in the following section on petroleum industry applications, activation analysis also provides an alternative to the radioisotope tracer method for conducting wear tests.

Luminescence

The use of radium to provide self-luminous watch dials and markers has been familiar for many years. Various beta-emitting radioisotopes, such as tritium or krypton 85, can also be used to produce visible light and are less hazardous than radium. They are accordingly being used increasingly for signal lights and markers of various kinds. Airlines are beginning to use the isotope sources in "Exit" signs because they are reliable and self-powered.

Static Dissipation

The fact that nuclear radiation ionizes material it strikes has been used to dissipate the electrostatic charges generated in many industrial processes. If not dissipated these charges can cause electric shock or the destructive accumulation of dust. When alpha particles or beta particles from a radioactive source ionize molecules of gases in the air, the air in effect becomes a conductor of electricity and provides a path for static electricity to drain off. This application is growing in industry, particularly in the paper industry.

Applications in the Petroleum Industry

Crude Oil Production

To learn about geological strata in oil wells, a radiation detector can be lowered into the well and its output continuously recorded as it is lowered. Four variants of this method of well "logging" are employed: (1) If a gamma detector is lowered it will record the natural radio-activity in ordinary rock. When it reaches oil, water, or a porous zone, the gamma signal will be decreased markedly.
(2) Water or oil-bearing strata can also be located by lowering a source which emits fast neutrons along with a detector of slow neutrons. When a hydrogenous zone is reached, signals detected will increase since hydrogenous materials slow down neutrons more efficiently than do other materials. (3) Another technique is based on the principles employed in density gaging. A sealed gamma source is lowered into the well along with a gamma detector shielded from the source. The gamma rays scattered from the walls of the well indicate rock densities.
(4) Finally, by lowering a gamma ray detector along with a neutron source, and measuring the characteristic gamma rays produced when neutrons are captured, the presence of specific elements (e.g., chlorine) in the strata can be detected. Nuclear logs are now made on a high percentage of wells drilled in the United States.

To increase the flow of oil from oil-bearing sandstone, the porosity of the strata is increased by forcing acid into them under pressure. To do this effectively it is necessary to know when acid poured into the well has reached the level at which treatment is to be made. A radiation detector is placed in the well at the desired level. A radioisotope is mixed with the acid. An increased signal from the detector reveals when the acid has filled the well to the desired level.

Radioisotopes are also used to detect flow channels that may carry oil away from wells. A suspension of radioactive particles is pumped through the well so that most of them lodge in permeable zones which can then be mapped by lowering a detector. An alternative method for checking on permeable zones is to inject tagged water or gas. Detectors

lowered into other bore holes in the field then show how much of the injected fluid has been carried away and in what direction.

Pipeline Operations

Radiographs are taken of welds in pipeline joints in order to inspect the welds for defects. This can be done when the pipeline is under construction by mounting a source inside the pipeline and pushing it along until it is in the same plane as a new weld. A strip of film is then wrapped around the outside of the weld and the radiograph is recorded. If any defects are disclosed they can then be repaired while the welding apparatus is still in the vicinity.

Advance predictions can be made of corrosion rates in pipelines. A section of pipe is irradiated and then the fluid for which it is to be used is passed through it at the expected operating rate. The level of radioactivity found in the fluid will indicate the rate at which the pipe may deteriorate.

Obstructions in pipelines are located by sending a radioisotope source through the pipeline in a carrier that will be blocked by the obstruction. A detector which has followed the source will then reveal the point of obstruction.

Underground pipelines are checked frequently for leaks because of the risk that they may pollute water supplies. A small amount of a short-lived radio-isotope is injected into the line. A part will escape at the point of a leak. Later a small device which detects and makes a recording of the presence of radioactivity is towed through the pipe. The device will detect the radioactivity which has leaked into the surrounding soil at the point of the leak, which can then be located readily by its place on the recording. The radioisotope dissipates itself in a short time.

Two methods are employed to mark the interface between petroleum products shipped by pipeline. One is to inject a small amount of radioisotope tracer at the point of interface. This can be detected when it reaches a receiving terminal or switching station so that each batch can be properly diverted. The alternative method involves density gaging. A source is placed on one side of the pipeline

The first demonstration of the use of radio-isotope tracers to mark the interface of fluids in a pipeline. One millicurie of barium 140 was injected in oil-soluble form into a stream of oil in a 20-inch pipe. Here, five miles away, a radiochemist awaits the signal from the tracer marking the interface, while a refinery operator stands ready to switch the flow of the stock following the interface into another tank.

The first routine industrial use of radiotracers was for the marking of interfaces between petroleum products shipped by pipeline from Salt Lake City, Utah, to Pasco, Washington. The technique has been in daily use on this pipeline since it began operating on June 6, 1950. Here the mechanic is installing piping under the heavily shielded vessel in which radioactive antimony 124 is to be stored. Routine injections are controlled entirely by controls outside the cabinet.

The petroleum refinery technician is flushing a fraction of a millicurie of tracer into a high-pressure injector. Subsequently it will be injected into the refinery stream. This is a standard operating technique for a wide variety of troubleshooting operations: measurement of flow rates, leak tests in heat exchangers, mixing in tanks, entrainment in stills, distillation efficiency, residence time in reactors, to mention a few.

and a detector on the other. The amount of radiation reaching the detector will change when the density of the material changes, thus signalling the arrival of the interface.

Refining Operations

The literature is replete with examples of tracer work in refinery operations. Catalyst flow rates have been measured quite successfully in solid flow circulating systems. Activated catalyst beads impregnated with zirconium 95 are available commercially. Two detectors are mounted on the downcomer pipe and fed to a common recording ratemeter. Instrumentation is available commercially for using this method in routine plant control.

In closed systems with good mixing the inventory volume can be estimated by the dilution method. A known amount of radioactivity is introduced, and after sufficient time to allow complete mixing, the final concentration is found by counting a sample. This method has been used to estimate the amount of sulfuric acid in an alkylation plant and the total catalyst inventory in a fluid cat cracker.

Other radioisotope applications that have been made in petroleum refining include determination of the degree of mixing in tar bottoms, the detection of cross leaking in heat exchangers, and the determination of the time between the point where a principle process variable is controlled and the first point where its effect can be measured.

Recently radiotracer techniques have been used for highly sophisticated analysis of catalyst residence time distributions in complex reaction vessels, such as the regenerator of a catalytic cracking unit. During the tracer test, samples of catalyst are withdrawn from various locations in the reaction vessel. Consideration of the time required for passage of a peak of radioactivity past each of the sampling points and the geometry of the vessel indicates the flow pattern of catalyst. Making use of an empirical observation that, after passage of the peak concentration of a tracer mixing into a vessel of the particular type studied, the concentration assumes a logarithmic relationship to the residence time, an analysis of catalyst residence time

Several oil refineries have used radioactive catalyst beads to measure circulation rates of catalyst through the reactor, where cracking occurs, and through the regenerator, where deposited coke is burned off the beads. On this standpipe at the top of the 300 foot high plant, Geiger counters at the top and bottom signal the passage of radioactive beads. One or two such beads are timed to control the circulation rate of the 10 billion ordinary beads in the plant.

distribution can be made. Studies of this sort not only serve as guidance in the design of additional reactors of the same or similar type, but in addition are valuable to the operating engineer in making changes in operating variables on the existing unit.

Product Evaluation

Ingenious wear tests have been devised to test the relative merits of various lubricants. Automobile engine oils with or without additives have been tested by making the engine's piston rings radioactive, and then, after the engine has been operated under various conditions of speed, temperature and the like, monitoring the crank case oil for radioactive wear particles. This procedure provides a continuous measurement of wear without need to assemble and disassemble the engine. It shows how much steady wear occurs under each operating condition and also what the effect is when operating conditions change. It has shown conclusively, for example, that wear is comparatively high before the engine has reached normal operating temperatures and comparatively low thereafter.

An alternative method of wear measurement is based on activation analysis. It can be employed on any engine, since no engine parts need be made radioactive. Instead, a sample of engine oil is irradiated and then analyzed for metal content which indicates wear.

A Note about Savings

The calculation of savings obtained by a radioisotope technique over an alternative technique is often not necessarily a true index of the significance of the application because the alternative in some cases could not have been used, and in other cases would not have used, so that the information obtained simply would not have been gained. The major contribution of the use of radioisotopes in the petroleum industry, and in other industries as well, has thus been to make improvements in processes and products which ultimately reflect themselves in an improved standard of living.

Closeup of several geiger counters mounted on standpipe.

Apparatus used to measure wear of piston rings in automotive engines. The pistons are first made radioactive by exposure to neutrons in a reactor. After operation of the engine under various test conditions, the amount of radioactivity found in the engine oil indicates the extent of piston wear.

Studying the Environment

Radiation techniques are being used increasingly in studies of man's environment. An important recent example has been the development of a device for precise and accurate measurement of slow moving ocean currents. Oceanographers have been handicapped by lack of such knowledge.

Known as "DWICA" (Deep Water Isotopic Current Analyzer) the device consists of a radioisotope injection mechanism in the center of a wagon-wheel configuration (approximately 30 inches in diameter) of radiation detectors.

DWICA is designed so that it can be lowered to a stationary position on the ocean floor. A radioisotope such as iodine 131 is then injected. By noting the time when the radioactivity is sensed by one or more of the detectors, the direction and rate of currents can be determined. Computer logic circuitry is employed to integrate the count rate and automatically print out the rate and direction of current drift.

Previous methods for determining the direction and flow rates of water currents have lacked accuracy because they involved the use of moving parts. For example, one system utilizes a rotor mounted on a sapphire bearing. No matter how well a rotative cup is designed, there will always be a certain amount of friction. While the effect of this may be scarcely noticeable at high velocities, it can have an important effect on the accuracy of measurement at low velocities.

A shallow water version of DWICA was used during 1961 to collect data on summer and winter cycles in Chesapeake Bay. The current model, which can measure velocities in the range from .001 to 1 knot, underwent calibration tests at the U. S. Navy's David Taylor Model Basin near Washington in January 1964.

It was successfully demonstrated in ocean tests off Bermuda at depths up to 200 feet in March 1964. Further tests at ocean depths up to one mile were planned for later in the year.

DWICA was invented and developed for the USAEC by the W. H. Johnston Laboratories, Baltimore, Md.

Another potentially important environmental study with radioisotopes has involved measuring the density of the upper atmosphere. Such measurements can be important to the understanding of meteorological phenomena and to the design and performance of advanced space planes and reentry vehicles. Measurements undertaken in the past have employed indirect and frequently inaccurate thermistor methods. Accordingly, the U. S. Air Force, Weather Bureau, and AEC have cooperated in an effort to develop a balloon sonde which uses a beta forward-scattering technique for direct measurement of atmospheric densities, which are then telemetered to the ground. The investigation for the three Agencies was conducted by Parametrics, Inc. of Waltham, Massachusetts.

The device employs a forward scatter gas density gage, consisting of a radioactive source maintained 14 inches from a radioisotope detector. The principle involved is that with fixed separation increasing densities of the intervening medium attenuate or decrease the rate at which the source emanations arrive at the detector while, conversely, decreasing densities give rise to increasing detector response. Forward scatter geometry is employed because it gives a better signal-to-noise ratio than backscatter geometry.

Flight tests of the device, using Krypton 85 as the source, have indicated an average error in the interval from 45,000 to 140,000 feet of $\pm$ 0.05%.

Planned for soft landing on the Moon is an instrument package that will use neutron activation analysis to obtain knowledge of the physical and chemical makeup of the surface of the Moon. In this method, a miniature nuclear accelerator ($\sim$6 cm long, 3 cm in dia) produces neutrons that interact with materials of the lunar surface. The gamma rays resulting from these interactions

are then detected in a scintillator, the output of which is recorded in a pulse-height analyzer. This information, stored in the analyzer memory, is later telemetered back to Earth. Since the gamma rays have energies that are characteristic of the elements present in the lunar surface, the energy spectra allow one to make a quantitative elemental analysis of the Moon's surface material.

Dr. Paul C. Aebersold, Director of USAEC's Division of Isotopes Development (right), inspects model of device intended for analyzing constituents of moon's surface.

Opposite:
Closeup of "DWICA" device used to measure the velocity of water currents at various depths below the surface.

Law enforcement

Ultrasensitive radiation techniques have recently demonstrated their usefulness in uncovering evidence valuable in solving crimes. The technique employed most commonly is neutron activation analysis. As was pointed out in the section on medical research, this technique permits the identification of trace elements in extremely small quantities in a substance by first making it radioactive and then noting the energies and half lives of the emitted gamma rays. The analysis can be made quantitative by comparing the results with those for control samples of known composition. This method, while still relatively new, has already made possible some criminal investigation methods of startling precision.

For example, late in 1960 the Oak Ridge National Laboratory started to compile by activation analysis the isotopic spectra of opium samples from countries throughout the world. Based on this work it is now possible, utilizing computer techniques, quickly to determine the geographical origin of seized opium by comparing its activation analysis spectrum with those of the control samples. This procedure may prove of great value in enforcing the international agreement reached by many countries through the Economic and Social Council of the UN to control the flow and production of opium.

The United States Internal Revenue Service (IRS) has been employing activation analysis with marked success in its enforcement activities directed against illegal traffic in narcotics and alcoholic beverages. Following are three recent examples:

(1) Suspects were apprehended in Los Angeles in September 1963 with over 400 one-pound plastic bags containing marihuana. It was suspected that one of the men was the producer and seller of marihuana seized from defendants in prior cases. This could be proved if it could be demonstrated that the marihuana involved in this case was grown in the same geographical area as that in the prior cases, and that the plastic bags were made by the same manufacturer. (Analyses previously performed on marihuana from different areas had shown

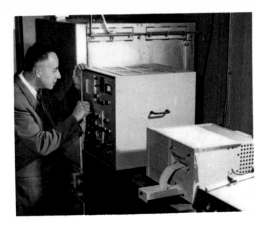

Maynard J. Pro, a scientist of the U.S. Internal Revenue Service, at work in the Department's activation analysis laboratory.

Molten paraffin being applied to back of gun hand of a "suspect" as first step in experimental test of activation analysis identification technique.

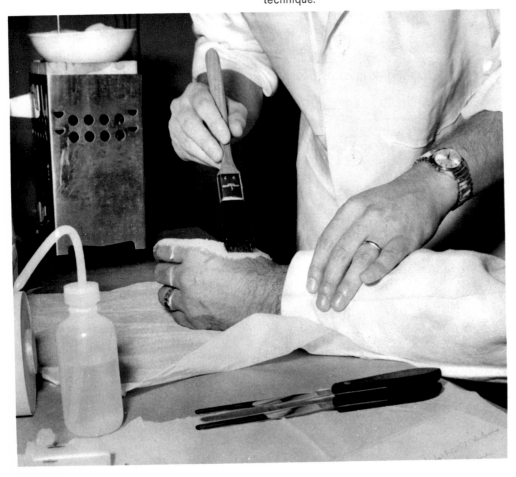

that, as in the case of opium, each had a unique elemental makeup; previous analysis of plastic bag material had shown that exact composition varied as between manufacturers.) Samples were forwarded to Maynard J. Pro, a scientist at IRS's Washington headquarters, and a pioneer in the application of radiation techniques to crime detection. Activation analysis performed by Mr. Pro, following irradiation of the samples in the reactor of the Armed Forces Radiobiology Institute in Bethesda, Maryland, provided the necessary proofs—the several marihuana samples had identical isotopic composition, as did the plastic bags. The suspected producer was tried and found guilty of transporting and possessing marihuana.

(2) Four men were arrested charged with conspiracy in connection with an illicit distillery in Georgia. The first man brought to trial was convicted in March 1964 based on evidence supplied by neutron activation analysis. This evidence showed that mud samples from the defendant's truck, picked up in Brooklyn, New York, exactly matched other mud samples from a Georgia road leading to the still.

(3) Illicit rice alcoholic distillates were seized from two bootleggers in San Francisco. Activation analysis was employed to determine whether the distillates were produced by the same still. The results indicated that two stills were involved. This provided excellent investigative evidence on the basis of which the two stills were sought and located.

The matching capabilities of activation analysis open up many other possibilities for criminal detection. Thus, tiny strands of hair, specks of dirt, flecks of paint, spots of grease, etc., left behind at the scene of a crime can be tested against similar substances belonging to a suspect. Conversely, such materials found on suspects can be matched with similar items at the crime scene. Much work in developing these possibilities has been done at ORNL.

Experimental work done at General Atomic has shown that, by activation analysis of minute residues left behind on the hands by exploding ammunition, it has been possible to determine whether

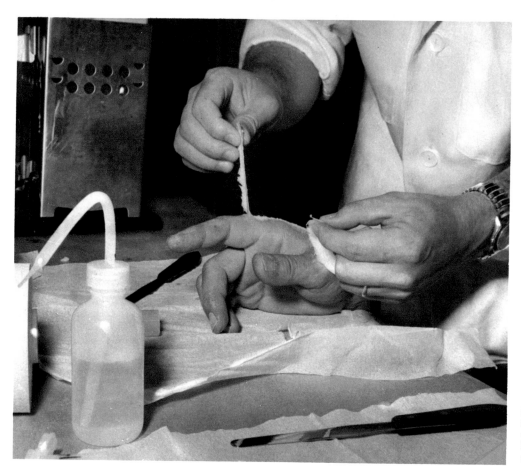

an individual has fired a gun, from which hand, and even the type of ammunition used.

From the examples given it can be seen that the usefulness of activation analysis in crime investigation is its unique ability to match substances of unknown origin with other substances of known origin. There appears to be no alternative analytical technique which is as sensitive and selective in making positive identification, although several have been tried, including infrared and ultraviolet spectroscopy, X ray diffraction and gas chromatography. Another advantage of activation analysis is that it does not damage the tested specimen, which can therefore be submitted later as court evidence if necessary.

Removing the paraffin cast from the "suspect's" hand. The paraffin is then irradiated in a reactor, after which traces of barium and antimony (components of bullet primers) resulting from blowback onto the hand during firing can be detected.

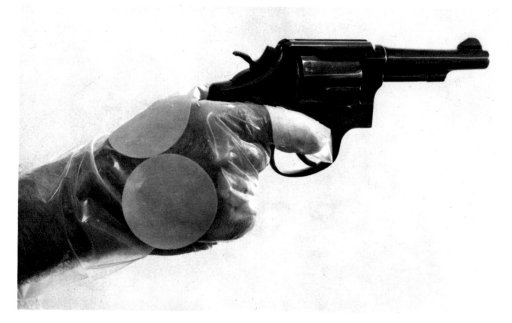

Test-firing a revolver using a plastic glove and moist filter paper. Activation analysis of the filter paper after it is irradiated will disclose the distribution of barium and antimony deposits on the gun hand.

Acknowledgments

The following persons were especially helpful to the authors in the preparation of this volume:

Paul C. Aebersold, Ph.D., U. S. Atomic Energy Commission

Axel L. Anderson, Ph.D., Michigan State University

H. O. Anger, Donner Laboratory, University of California, Berkeley

Charles Artandi, Ph.D., Ethicon, Inc.

William G. Baird, Jr., W. R. Grace Co.

Philip S. Baker, Oak Ridge National Laboratory

Alvah V. Barron, Jr., Industrial Nucleonics

J. E. Beach, E. I. duPont de Nemours and Co.

Oscar M. Bizzell, U. S. Atomic Energy Commission

James L. Born, M.D., Donner Laboratory

John C. Brown, Ph.D., U. S. Department of Agriculture

H. D. Bruner, M.D., U. S. Atomic Energy Commission

Harvey A. Burley, General Motors Corp.

W. W. Burr, Jr., M.D., U. S. Atomic Energy Commission

J. W. J. Carpender, M.D., Argonne Cancer Research Hospital

George C. Cotzias, M.D., Brookhaven National Laboratory

Howard J. Curtis, Ph.D., Brookhaven National Laboratory

G. J. D'Angio, M.D., Children's Hospital, Boston

Charles L. Dunham, M.D., U. S. Atomic Energy Commission

Robert L. Dunne, Esso Research and Engineering Co.

D. H. Etzler, California Research Corp.

Samuel A. Goldblith, Ph.D., Massachusetts Institute of Technology

Kenneth D. Goodrich, U. S. Department of Agriculture

John Grebe, Ph.D., Dow Chemical Co.

Vincent P. Guinn, Ph.D., General Atomic

David E. Harmer, Ph.D., Dow Chemical Co.

Paul V. Harper, M.D., Argonne Cancer Research Hospital

George R. Hawkes, California Chemical Co.

Lyman S. Henderson, Ph.D., U. S. Department of Agriculture

Sterling Hendricks, Ph.D., U. S. Department of Agriculture

W. L. Hill, U. S. Department of Agriculture

Norman N. Hochgraft, Esso Research and Engineering Co.

Walter L. Hughes, Tufts University School of Medicine, Boston

Donald E. Hull, California Research Corp.

W. D. Hunt, Instruments, Inc.

Edward S. Josephson, Ph.D., QMRE Command, U. S. Army

Edward F. Knipling, U. S. Department of Agriculture

Otto A. Kuhl, Brookhaven National Laboratory

John L. Kuranz, Nuclear-Chicago Corp.

F. W. Lanard, M.D., U. S. Atomic Energy Commission

Joseph Machurek, U. S. Atomic Energy Commission

Edward L. Maxie, University of California

William G. Myers, The Ohio State University School of Medicine, Columbus

Tove Neville, University of California, Berkeley

William T. Pentzer, U. S. Department of Agriculture

Myron Pollycove, M.D., Donner Laboratory

Maynard J. Pro, U. S. Internal Revenue Service

Roger J. Romani, Ph.D., University of California

George J. Rotariu, Ph.D., U. S. Atomic Energy Commission

Arthur F. Rupp, Oak Ridge National Laboratory

T. W. Sargent, Ph.D., Donner Laboratory

Kevin G. Shea, Ph.D., U. S. Atomic Energy Commission

W. E. Siri, Donner Laboratory

Joseph W. Slavin, Ph.D., U. S. Department of Interior

Meyer Steinberg, Brookhaven National Laboratory

Harold Smith, Ph.D., Brookhaven National Laboratory

Alexander Sommerville, Ph.D., General Motors Corp.

Frank G. Sorenson, Jr., Ohmart Corp.

Martin H. Stein, U. S. Atomic Energy Commission

Loren F. Steiner, Ph.D., U. S. Department of Agriculture

Christopher G. Stevenson, General Electric Co.

Charles Stoops, Ph.D., Phillips Petroleum Co.

James Sutherland, Ph.D., Brookhaven National Laboratory

C. A. Tobias, Ph.D., Donner Laboratory

Dr. K. C. Tsien, International Atomic Energy Agency

D. C. Van Dyke, M.D., Donner Laboratory

D. M. Wilkes, Lawrence Radiation Laboratory

H. S. Winchell, M.D., Donner Laboratory

Robert W. Wood, Ph.D., U. S. Atomic Energy Commission

Photo Credits

Albert Einstein Medical Center,
  Philadelphia
M. D. Anderson Hospital, Texas
Argonne Cancer Research Hospital
Argonne National Laboratory
Boston University Medical Center
Brookhaven National Laboratory
California Chemical Co.
Donner Laboratory, University of
  California (Berkeley)
Dow Chemical Co.
E. I. Dupont de Nemours & Co.
Esso Research and Engineering Co.
General Atomic
General Electric Co.
General Motors Corp.
W. R. Grace & Co.
Industrial Nucleonics Corp.
Johns Hopkins Medical Institute
W. H. Johnston Laboratories
Los Alamos Scientific Laboratory
Massachusetts General Hospital
Wayne Miller, Magnum Photos
Nuclear Chicago Corp.
Oak Ridge Institute of Nuclear Studies
Oak Ridge National Laboratory
Phillips Petroleum Co.
Roswell Park Memorial Institute
Sloan-Kettering Institute
Texas A. & M. University
U.S. Army Quartermaster Corps
U.S. Department of Agriculture
U.S. Veterans Administration Hospital,
  Los Angeles
University of California, Davis
University of Chicago
University of Pennsylvania
University of Rochester
University of Washington School
  of Medicine
Robert J. Walton
Washington University School of Medicine,
  St. Louis

Book Design: Rudolph deHarak
Typography: Linocraft, Inc.
Printing: Photogravure & Color, Inc.

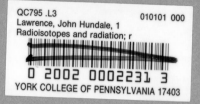